916.7
Sch9o

S0-BIB-511

DATE DUE			
Dec 2 '71			
Mar 16 '82			
GAYLORD M-2			PRINTED IN U.S.A.

WITHDRAWN
L. R. COLLEGE LIBRARY

ON THE EDGE OF
THE PRIMEVAL FOREST

By ALBERT SCHWEITZER

THE PHILOSOPHY OF CIVILIZATION

I. THE DECAY AND THE RESTORATION OF CIVILIZATION
Translated by C. T. Campion. Second Edition.

II. CIVILIZATION AND ETHICS
Translated by C. T. Campion. Second Edition.

III. THE WORLD-VIEW OF REVERENCE FOR LIFE
In preparation

IV. THE CIVILIZED STATE
In preparation

✱

THE QUEST OF THE HISTORICAL JESUS
Translated by W. Montgomery. Second Edition.

THE MYSTERY OF THE KINGDOM OF GOD
Translated by Walter Lowrie

PAUL AND HIS INTERPRETERS
A CRITICAL HISTORY
Translated by W. Montgomery, B.D.

THE MYSTICISM OF PAUL THE APOSTLE
Translated by W. Montgomery, B.D.

J. S. BACH
Translated by Ernest Newman. Two vols.

ON THE EDGE OF THE PRIMEVAL FOREST
EXPERIENCES AND OBSERVATIONS OF A DOCTOR
IN EQUATORIAL AFRICA
Translated by C. T. Campion. Eleventh Impression, illustrated.

✱

THE PATH TO RECONSTRUCTION
A BRIEF INTRODUCTION TO SCHWEITZER'S PHILOSOPHY OF CIVILIZATION
By Mrs. C. E. B. Russell

ALBERT SCHWEITZER:
HIS WORK AND HIS PHILOSOPHY
By Oskar Kraus
Introduction by A. D. Lindsay

ALBERT SCHWEITZER
PHILOSOPHER, THEOLOGIAN, MUSICIAN AND DOCTOR
Some Biographical Notes compiled by C. T. Campion. Illustrated.

✱

ADAM & CHARLES BLACK · SOHO SQUARE · LONDON W.1

LUMBERMEN AND TIMBER-RAFTS AT THE MOUTH OF THE OGOWE.

ON THE EDGE OF THE
PRIMEVAL FOREST

Experiences and Observations of
a Doctor in Equatorial Africa

by

ALBERT SCHWEITZER

D.THEOL., D.PHIL., D.MED., (STRASBOURG)

AUTHOR OF "THE QUEST OF THE HISTORICAL JESUS,"
"THE PHILOSOPHY OF CIVILIZATION," ETC.

TRANSLATED BY C. T. CAMPION

ELEVENTH IMPRESSION
WITH SIXTEEN PHOTOGRAPHS

CARL A. RUDISILL
LIBRARY
LENOIR RHYNE COLLEGE

ADAM AND CHARLES BLACK
4, 5 & 6 SOHO SQUARE LONDON W.1

916.7
916.7
Sch90
21905-
aug, 1946

DEDICATION

To the friends, dead and living,
who have helped me in the enterprise
of which this book is a part,
in deepest gratitude

MADE IN GREAT BRITAIN
FIRST PUBLISHED JANUARY 19TH, 1922
REPRINTED 1922, 1923, 1924,
1926, 1928, 1929, 1931, 1934, 1937 and 1944

CONTENTS

NOTE

With regard to the English Edition of this book I owe a debt of thanks to two friends. Mr. C. T. Campion. M.A., had the goodness to prepare and to put at my disposal his very excellent translation, and Mr. John Naish, of Oxford, was kind enough to revise the proofs and to undertake the final corrections.

ILLUSTRATIONS

Note.—I am indebted for a large part of the photographs to the kindness of a grateful patient. Illustrations Nos. 5 and 6 are based on a slide made by Mr. Ottmann. For illustration No. 3 I have to thank Mr. Pelot, and for Nos. 4 and 15 Mr. Morel.

SKETCH MAP OF THE LOWER COURSE OF THE OGOWE

ON THE EDGE OF THE PRIMEVAL FOREST

CHAPTER I

HOW I CAME TO BE A DOCTOR IN THE FOREST. THE LAND AND PEOPLE OF THE OGOWE

I GAVE up my position of professor in the University of Strasbourg, my literary work, and my organ-playing, in order to go as a doctor to Equatorial Africa. How did that come about?

I had read about the physical miseries of the natives in the virgin forests; I had heard about them from missionaries, and the more I thought about it the stranger it seemed to me that we Europeans trouble ourselves so little about the great humanitarian task which offers itself to us in far-off lands. The parable of Dives and Lazarus seemed to me to have been spoken directly of us! We are Dives, for, through the advances of medical science, we now know a great deal about disease and pain, and have innumerable means of fighting them: yet we take as a matter of course the incalculable advantages which this new wealth gives us! Out there in the colonies, however, sits wretched Lazarus, the coloured folk, who suffers from illness

and pain just as much as we do, nay, much more, and
has absolutely no means of fighting them.   And just
as Dives sinned against the poor man at his gate
because for want of thought he never put himself in
his place and let his heart and conscience tell him what
he ought to do, so do we sin against the poor man at
our gate.

*

*   *

The two or three hundred doctors whom the European States maintain as medical officers in the colonial
world could undertake only a very small part (so I
argued to myself) of the huge task, even if the majority
of them were not there for the benefit, first of all, of the
white colonists and the troops.   Society in general
must recognise this work of humanity to be its task,
and there must come a time when doctors go out into
the world of their own free will, but sent and supported
by society and in numbers corresponding to the need,
to work for the benefit of the natives.   Then only
shall we be recognising and beginning to act upon the
responsibility in respect of the coloured races which
lies upon us as inheritors of the world's civilisation.

Moved by these thoughts I resolved, when already
thirty years old, to study medicine and to put my
ideas to the test out there.   At the beginning of 1913
I graduated as M.D.   That same spring I started with
my wife, who had qualified as a nurse, for the River
Ogowe in Equatorial Africa, there to begin my active
work.

I chose this locality because some Alsatian missionaries in the service of the Paris Evangelical Mission

had told me that a doctor was badly needed there on account of the constantly spreading sleeping sickness. The mission was prepared also to place at my disposal one of the houses at their station at Lambarene, and to allow me to build a hospital in their grounds, promising further to give me help with the work.

The actual expenses of the undertaking, however, I had to provide myself, and to that I devoted what I had earned by giving organ concerts, together with the profits from my book on Bach, which had appeared in German, French, and English. In this way the old Thomas Cantor of Leipsig, Johann Sebastian himself, helped me in the provision of a hospital for negroes in the virgin forest, and kind friends in Germany, France, and Switzerland contributed money. When we left Europe, the undertaking was securely financed for two years, the expenses—apart from the journey out and back—being, as I reckoned, about 15,000 francs* a year, and this calculation proved to be very nearly correct.

The keeping of the accounts and the ordering of all the things needed had been undertaken by self-sacrificing friends in Strasbourg, and the cases, when packed, were sent to Africa by the mission with their own.

My work then lived—to use a scientific term—in symbiosis with the Paris Evangelical Mission, but it was, in itself, undenominational and international. It was, and is still, my conviction that the humanitarian work to be done in the world should, for its accomplishment, call upon us as men, not as members of any particular nation or religious body.

---

* *I.e.*, about £600 p.a. at the then normal rate of exchange.

Now for a word about the country which was the scene of our labours. The Ogowe district belongs to the Colony of Gaboon, and the Ogowe itself is a river, 700 to 800 miles long, north of, and roughly parallel to, the Congo. Although smaller than the latter, it is yet a magnificent river, and in the lower part of its course its width is from 1,200 to 2,200 yards. For the last 120 miles it divides into a number of arms which enter the Atlantic near Cape Lopez, but it is navigable for fairly large river steamers as far as N'Djôle, about 250 miles up stream. At that point begins the region of hills and mountains which leads up to the great plateau of Central Africa. Here also begins a series of rapids which alternate with stretches of ordinary open river, and these rapids can only be surmounted by small screw steamers, built for the purpose, and by native canoes.

While along the middle and upper course of the Ogowe the country is a mixture of prairie and wood, there is along the lower part of the river, from N'Djôle downwards, nothing but water and virgin forest. This damp, low-lying ground is admirably suited for the cultivation of coffee, pepper, cinnamon, vanilla, and cocoa ; the oil palm also grows well in it. But the chief ·business of Europeans is neither the cultivation of these things, nor the collection of rubber in the forest, but the timber trade. Now on the west coast of Africa, which is very poor in harbours, especially in such as have rivers discharging into them, conditions are very seldom favourable for the loading of timber cargoes. But the Ogowe has the great advantage of discharging into an excellent roadstead without any bar ; the huge rafts can lie alongside the steamers which are to take them away without danger of being broken up and scattered on a bar or by a heavy swell. The timber trade, therefore, is likely to be for an indefinite period the chief industry of the Ogowe district.

Cereals and potatoes it is, unfortunately, impossible to cultivate, since the warm, damp atmosphere makes them grow too fast. Cereals never produce the usual ear, and potato haulms shoot up without any tubers below. Rice, too, is for various reasons not cultivable. Cows cannot be kept along the lower Ogowe because they cannot eat the grass that grows there, though further inland, on the central plateau, they flourish splendidly. It is necessary, therefore, to import from Europe flour, rice, potatoes, and milk, a fact which makes living a complicated business and very expensive.

Lambarene lies a little south of the Equator, so that its seasons are those of the Southern hemisphere: winter when it is summer in Europe, and *vice versâ*. Its winter is characterised by its including the dry season, which lasts from the end of May to the beginning of October, and summer is the rainy season, the rain falling from early in October to the middle of December, and from the middle of January to the end of May. About Christmas one gets three to four weeks of continuous summer weather, and it is then that the thermometer record is highest.

The average shade temperature in the rainy season is 82°—86° F.,* in the dry season about 77°—82° F., the nights being always nearly as hot as the days. This circumstance, and the excessive moisture of the

* *I.e.*, 28° to 30° and 25° to 28° C.

atmosphere, are the chief things which make the climate of the Ogowe lowlands such a trial for a European. After a year's residence fatigue and anæmia begin to make themselves disagreeably perceptible. At the end of two or three years he becomes incapable of real work, and does best to return to Europe for at least eight months in order to recruit.

The mortality among the whites at Libreville, the capital of Gaboon, was, in 1903, 14 per cent.

*

*   *

Before the war there lived in the Ogowe lowlands about two hundred whites : planters, timber merchants, storekeepers, officials, and missionaries. The number of the natives is hard to estimate, but, at any rate, the country is not thickly inhabited. We have at present merely the remains of eight once powerful tribes, so terribly has the population been thinned by three hundred years of alcohol and the slave trade. Of the Orungu tribe, which lived in the Ogowe delta, there are scarcely any left ; of the Galoas, who belonged to the Lambarene district, there remain still 80,000 at most. Into the void thus created there swarmed from inland the cannibal Fans, called by the French Pahouins, who have never yet come into contact with civilisation, and but for the opportune arrival of the Europeans this warrior folk would by this time have eaten up the old tribes of the Ogowe lowlands. Lambarene forms in the river valley the boundary between the Pahouins and the old tribes.

Gaboon was discovered by the Portuguese at the end of the fifteenth century, and by 1521 there was a Catholic mission settlement on the coast between the mouths of the Congo and the Ogowe. Cape Lopez is named after one of them, Odoardo Lopez, who came out there in 1578. In the eighteenth century the Jesuits had extensive plantations on the coast, with thousands of slaves, but they were as far from penetrating to the hinterland as were the white traders.

When, in the middle of the nineteenth century, the French and the English combined to fight the slave trade on the west coast, they chose, in 1849, the bay which lies north of that of Cape Lopez for the headquarters of their fleet, establishing there also a settlement to which they could send the rescued slaves : hence the name Libreville. That the narrow channels which empty themselves here and there into Cape Lopez bay belonged to a great river, the whites did not yet know, for the natives inhabiting the coast had withheld the information in order to keep the inland trade in their own hands. It was not till 1862 that Lieut. Serval, while on an excursion to the south-east of Libreville, discovered the Ogowe in the neighbourhood of Lambarene. Then began the exploration, from Cape Lopez, of the lower course of the river, and the chiefs were gradually brought to acknowledge the French protectorate.

When in the eighties the need was felt of finding the most convenient route for trade from the coast up to the navigable parts of the Congo, de Brazza believed that it was to be found in the Ogowe, since this river rises only some 125 miles north-west of Stanley Pool, and is separated from the Alima, a navigable tributary of the Congo, only by a narrow watershed. He even succeeded in getting to the Congo by this route a steamer which could be taken to pieces and transported by land, but the route proved to be impracticable for trade on account of the difficulties caused by the rapids in the upper part of the Ogowe. The construction of the Belgian-Congo railway between Matadi and Brazzaville was finished in 1898, and this put a final end to any idea of making the Ogowe a way to the Congo. To-day the Ogowe is used only by the traffic which goes up to its own still comparatively unexplored hinterland.

The first Protestant missionaries on the Ogowe were Americans, who came there about 1860, but as they could not comply with the requirement of the French Government that they should give their school instruction in French, they resigned their work later on to the Paris Missionary Society.

To-day this society owns four stations: N'Gômô, Lambarene, Samkita, and Talagouga. N'Gômô is about 140 miles from the coast, and the others follow one another in that order at intervals of about 35 miles. Talagouga is situated on a picturesque island just in front of N'Djôle, which is the farthest point to which the river steamer goes.

At each Protestant mission station there are generally one unmarried and two married missionaries, and, as a rule, a woman teacher also, making five or six persons, without reckoning the children.

The Catholic mission has three stations in the same district: one in Lambarene, one in N'Djôle, and one near Samba, on the N'Gounje, the largest tributary of the Ogowe, and on each station there live about ten whites: usually three priests, two lay brothers, and five sisters.

The administrative officials of the district are

stationed at Cape Lopez, at Lambarene, at Samba, and at N'Djôle, with about five hundred coloured soldiers distributed over it to act as a police force.

Such was the country, and such the people among whom for four and a half years I worked as the forest doctor. What I experienced during that time and the observations I made previous to the outbreak of the war, I shall now describe with the help of the reports which I wrote every six months in Lambarene and sent as printed letters to my friends and supporters. During the war such correspondence was, of course, impossible, and for that later period and for what is said about the religious and social problems treated of, I rely on memoranda which I made for my own use.

CHAPTER II

THE JOURNEY

LAMBARENE, *July*, 1913.

THE church bells in my native Alsatian village of Günsbach, in the Vosges, had just ceased ringing for the afternoon service on Good Friday, 1913, when the train appeared round the corner of the wood, and the journey to Africa began. We waved our farewells from the platform of the last coach, and for the last time saw the *flêche* on the church tower peeping up among the trees. When should we see them again ? When next day Strasbourg Cathedral sank out of sight we seemed to be already in a foreign land.

On Easter Sunday we heard once more the dear old organ of S. Sulpice's Church in Paris and the wonderful playing of our friend Widor. At two o'clock the Bordeaux train glided out of the underground station at the Quai d'Orsay, and we began a delightful journey. Everywhere we saw people in their holiday dress ; the sunshine was brilliant, and the warm spring breeze brought out of the distance the sound of the village church bells, which seemed to be greetings to the train that was hurrying past. It was an Easter Day which seemed a glorious dream.

The Congo steamers do not start from Bordeaux but from Pauillac, which is an hour and a half by train nearer the sea. But I had to get my big packing case, which had been sent in advance by goods train, out of the custom house at Bordeaux, and this was closed on Easter Monday. There would have been no time on Tuesday to manage it, but fortunately an official observed and was touched by our anxiety, and enabled me to get possession of my goods without all the prescribed formalities. But it was only at the last minute that two motor cars got us and our belongings to the harbour station, where the train was already waiting which was to convey the passengers for the Congo to their ship. The feeling of relief can hardly be described with which, after all the excitement and the payment of all those who had helped us off, we sank into our seats in the railway carriage. The guard blew his whistle; the soldiers who were also going took their places; we moved out into the open, and for a time had the enjoyment of blue sky and pleasant breeze, with the sight here and there of water, and yellow broom in flower, and cows quietly grazing. In an hour and a half we are at the quay among packing cases, bales, and barrels, ten yards from the ship, called the *Europe*, which is gently tossing on the somewhat restless waters of the Gironde. Then came a time of crushing, shouting, signalling to porters; we push and are pushed till, over the narrow gangway, we get on board and, on giving our names, learn the number of the cabin which is to be our home for three whole weeks. It is a roomy one, well forward and away from the engines, which is a great advantage. Then we had just time to wash before the bell rang for lunch.

We had at our table several officers, the ship's doctor, an army doctor, and two wives of colonial officials who were returning to their husbands after a voyage home to recruit. All of them, as we soon discovered, had already been in Africa or in other colonies, so that we felt ourselves to be poor untravelled home birds. I could not help thinking of the fowls my mother used to buy every summer from Italian poultry dealers to add to her stock, and which for several days used to walk about among the old ones very shyly and humbly ! One thing that struck me as noticeable in the faces of our fellow travellers was a certain expression of energy and determination.

As there was still a great deal of cargo to come aboard we did not start till the following afternoon, when under a gloomy sky we drew slowly down the Gironde. As darkness gradually set in the long roll of the waves told us that we had reached the open sea, and about nine o'clock the last shimmering lights had disappeared.

Of the Bay of Biscay the passengers told each other horrid tales. " How I wish it were behind us ! " we heard at every meal-time, but we were to make full proof of its malice. On the second day after starting a regular storm set in, and the ship pitched and tossed like a great rocking-horse, and rolled from starboard to port, and back from port to starboard, with impartial delight. The Congo boats do this more than others in a heavy sea because, in order to be able to ascend the river as far as Matadi, whatever the state of the water, they are of a comparatively shallow build.

Being without experience of ocean travel, I had forgotten to make the two cabin trunks fast with cords, and in the night they began to chase each other about. The two hat cases also, which contained our sun helmets, took part in the game without reflecting how badly off they might come in it, and when I tried to catch the trunks, I nearly got one leg crushed between them and the wall of the cabin. So I left them to their fate and contented myself with lying quietly in my berth and counting how many seconds elapsed between each plunge made by the ship and the corresponding rush of our boxes. Soon there could be heard similar noises from other cabins and, added to them, the sound of crockery, etc., moving wildly about in the galley and the dining saloon. With morning came a steward, who showed me the scientific way of making the baggage fast.

For three days the storm lasted with undiminished force. Standing or even sitting in the cabins or the saloons was not to be thought of; one was thrown about from one corner to the other, and several passengers received more or less serious injuries. On Sunday we had cold food only, because the cooks were unable to use the galley fire, and it was not till we were near Teneriffe that the storm abated.

I had been looking forward to the first sight of this island, which is always said to be so magnificent, but, alas! I overslept myself and woke only as we were entering the harbour. Then, scarcely had the anchor been dropped, when we were hemmed in on both sides by coaling-hulks from which were hoisted sacks of food for the engines, to be emptied through the hatches into the ship's hold.

Teneriffe lies on high ground which slopes rather steeply into the sea, and has all the appearance of a Spanish town. The island is carefully cultivated and produces potatoes enough to supply the whole coast of West Africa, besides bananas, early potatoes, and other vegetables for Europe.

We weighed anchor about three o'clock, and I stood in the bows and watched how the anchor slowly left the bottom and came up through the transparent water. I watched also, with admiration, what I took for a blue bird flying gracefully above the surface of the sea, till a sailor told me it was a flying fish.

Then, as we moved from the coast southwards, there rose slowly up behind the island the snow-capped summit of its highest mountain, till it lost itself in the clouds, while we steamed away over a gently heaving sea and admired the entrancing blue of the water.

It was during this portion of the voyage that we found it possible to become acquainted with one another. The other passengers were mostly army officers and doctors and civil service officials; it surprised me to find so few traders on board. The officials, as a rule, are told only where they are to land, and not until on shore do they get to know their ultimate destination.

Among those whom we got to know best were a lieutenant and a Government official. The latter was going to the Middle Congo region and had to leave his wife and children for two years. The lieutenant was in much the same position, and was expecting to go up to Abescher. He had already been in Tonquin, and in Madagascar, on the Senegal, the Niger, and the Congo, and he was interested in every department of colonial affairs. He held crushing views about Mahommedanism as it prevails among the natives, seeing in it the greatest danger there is for the future of Africa. "The Mahommedan negro," he said, "is no longer any good for anything. You may build him railways, dig him canals, spend hundreds of thousands of pounds to provide irrigation for the land he is to cultivate, but it all makes no impression on him ; he is absolutely and on principle opposed to everything European, however advantageous and profitable it may be. But let a marabout—a travelling preacher of Islam—come into the village on his ambling horse with his yellow cloak over his shoulders, then things begin to wake up ! Everybody crowds round him, and brings his savings in order to buy with hard cash charms against sickness, wounds, and snake bite, against bad spirits and bad neighbours. Wherever the negro population has turned Mahommedan there is no progress, either socially or economically. When we built the first railway in Madagascar, the natives stood for days together round the locomotive and wondered at it ; they shouted for joy when it let off steam, and kept trying to explain to each other how the thing could move. In an African town inhabited by Mahommedan negroes, the local water power was used once for an installation of electric light, and it was expected that the people would be surprised at the novel brightness. But the evening that the lamps were first used the whole population remained inside their houses and huts and discussed the matter there, so as to show their indifference to the novelty." *

Very valuable I found my acquaintance with a military doctor who had already had twelve years' experience of Equatorial Africa, and was going to Grand Bassam as director of the Bacteriological Institute there.

* In some African colonies Mahommedan negroes are more open to progress.

At my request he spared me two hours every morning, during which he gave me an account of the general system of tropical medicine, illustrated by his own experiments and experiences. It was very necessary, he thought, that as many independent doctors as possible should devote themselves to the care of the native population ; only so could we hope to get the mastery of the sleeping sickness.

The day after we left Teneriffe the troops were ordered to wear their sun-helmets whenever they were outside the saloons and cabins. This precaution struck me as noticeable, because the weather was still cool and fresh, hardly warmer than it is with us in June, but on the same day I got a warning from an " old African," as I was enjoying the sight of the sunset with nothing on my head. " From to-day onwards," he said, " you must, even though the weather is not yet hot, regard the sun as your worst enemy, and that whether it is rising, or high in heaven, or setting, and whether the sky is cloudy or not. Why this is so, and on what the sun's power depends, I cannot tell you, but you may take it from me that people get dangerous sunstrokes before they get close to the equator, and that the apparently mild heat of the rising or setting sun is even more treacherous than the full glow of that fiery body at mid-day."

At Dakar, the great harbour of the Colony of Senegambia, my wife and I set foot for the first time on the soil of Africa to which we were to devote our lives, and we felt it as a somewhat solemn moment. Of Dakar itself I have no kindly remembrance, for I cannot forget the cruelty to animals which is universal there. The town lies on a steep slope, the streets are mostly in very bad condition, and the lot of the poor beasts of burden which are at the mercy of the negroes is terrible : I have never seen such overworked horses and mules as here. On one occasion when I came on two negroes who were perched on a cart heavily laden with wood which had stuck in the newly mended street, and with loud shouts were belabouring their poor beast, I simply could not pass by, but compelled them to dismount and to push behind till the three of us got the cart on the move. They were much disconcerted, but obeyed without replying. " If you cannot endure to see animals ill-treated, don't go to Africa ! " said the lieutenant to me when I got back. " You will see plenty of that kind of horror here."

At this port we took on board a number of Senegalese tirailleurs with their wives and children. They lay about the foredeck, and at night crept, head and all, into big sacks, as they had to sleep in the open. The wives and children were heavily loaded with charms, enclosed in little leather bags, even the babies at the breast not being exempt.

The shores of Africa I had pictured to myself as desert, and when, on the way to Konakri, the next place of call to Dakar, we put in towards the coast, I was surprised to see nothing but magnificently green woods coming down right to the water's edge. With my telescope I could see the pointed huts of the negro villages, and rising between us and them, like a cloud, the spray of the waves on the bar ; the sea, however, was fairly calm, and the coast, so far as I could see, was flat.

" A shark ! A shark ! " I rushed from the writing saloon, and was shown a black triangular object

projecting from the water and moving in the direction
of the ship. It was a fin of that dreaded sea-monster,
and whoever has once seen it never forgets it or confuses
it with anything else. The West African harbours all
swarm with sharks. In Kotonou I saw one, enticed by
the kitchen refuse, come to about twelve yards from the
ship. The light being good and the water very transparent, I could see for several minutes the whole length
of its glistening grey and yellow body, and observe how
the creature turned over nearly on to its back to get
what it considered worth devouring into its mouth,
which, as we all know, is placed on the underside of its
head.

In spite of the sharks the negroes in all these harbours
are ready to dive for coins, and accidents seldom
happen to them, because the noise they make during
the proceedings gets on the nerves of even these
wolves of the sea. At Tabou I was astonished to see
one of the divers quite silent while the rest were crying
out for more coins, but I noticed later that he was the
most skilful of the lot and had to keep silent because
his mouth served as his purse, and he could hardly
shut it for the number of nickel and silver coins that
were in it.

From Konakri onwards we were almost always
within sight of the coast. The Pepper Coast, the Ivory
Coast, the Gold Coast, the Slave Coast ! If only that
line of forest on the horizon could tell us about all the
cruelty it has had to witness ! Here the slave dealers
used to land and ship their living cargoes for transport
to America. " It is not all as it should be, even to-
day," said to me an employee of a big trading firm,
who was returning for a third period of work to his post

in Africa. "We bring the negroes strong drink and diseases which were previously unknown among them. Do the blessings we bring the natives really outweigh the evils that go with them?"

Several times during meals I found myself watching the guests at the different tables. All had already worked in Africa, but with what objects? What ideals had they? So pleasant and friendly here, what sort of people were they away in their places of work? What responsibility did they feel? In a few days the three hundred of us who left Bordeaux together will have landed in Africa, and in a few weeks we shall be separated, taking up our duties on the Senegal, on the Niger, on the Ogowe, on the Congo and its tributaries, some even as far away as Lake Chad, to work in these different regions for three years or so. What shall we accomplish? If everything could be written down that is done during these years by all of us who are now here on this ship, what a book it would be! Would there be no pages that we should be glad to turn over as quickly as possible? . . .

But the ship is carrying us on and on. Grand Bassam . . . Kotonou . . . Each time there are hearty farewells exchanged between many who have hardly spoken to each other. "Good health to you!" The words are spoken with a smile, but again and again, and in this climate they have a serious sound. How will those to whom they are spoken look when they come on board next? And will they all come back? . . . The windlasses and cranes begin to creak; the boats are dancing on the waves; the red roofs of the seaside town throw us a bright greeting from out of the mass of greenery; the waves breaking on the sandy bar send

up their clouds of spray . . . and behind them all lies
the immeasurable stretch of land, at some place in
which every one who leaves us here is to be a lord and
master, all his doings having a significance of some sort
for the great land's future. " Good health to you !
Good health- to you ! "   It seems to be scarcely a
solemn enough farewell for all that lies in the future !

At Tabou and at Grand Bassam, on the Ivory Coast,
and at Kotonou, the swell is so heavy even in good
weather that passengers cannot get into the boats by
the rope-ladder, but must be lowered into them four
at a time in wooden boxes, such as one sees on merry-
go-rounds at village fairs.   It is the duty of the engineer
who manages the crane to seize the right moment for
letting the cradle with its four occupants safely down
into the bottom of the boat which is dancing up and
down on the waves ; the negro in the boat has to see
that his craft is exactly below the cradle as it descends,
and accidents are not infrequent.   The unloading of
cargo is also a very difficult operation and only possible in calm weather.   I now understand the assertions
that West Africa is very poor in good harbours.

At Tabou we took on board, as is done on every
voyage, some fifty negroes for handling the cargo.
They are taken as far as the Congo, to be landed again
on the return voyage, and they helped with the unloading at Libreville, Cape Lopez, and Matadi, the places
to which most of the freight is consigned.   They do
their work perfectly, almost better than the dock
labourers at Pauillac, but their behaviour towards the
other coloured folk on board is brutal.   Whenever the
latter get the least bit in their way they come to
blows.

A RIVER STEAMER ON THE OGOWE.

MY LITTLE BUNGALOW.

Above: Distant view, with orange and citron trees in the foreground: Below: Near view.

Every evening the glimmer of the sea, as the ship ploughs her way through it, is wonderful : the foam is phosphorescent, and little jelly-fishes spring up through it like glowing balls of metal. After leaving Konakri we saw almost every night the reflection of storms that swept across the country, and we passed through several deluges of rain accompanied by tornadoes that did nothing, however, to cool the air. On cloudy days the heat was worse than on others, and the sun, although not shining directly on us, was said to be much more dangerous in such weather than at other times.

Early on April 13th, a Sunday, we reached Libreville, and were welcomed by Mr. Ford, the American missionary, who brought us a preliminary gift from Africa of flowers and fruit from the mission-house garden. We thankfully accepted his invitation to visit the mission station, which is called Baraka, and is situated on a hill about 2½ miles along the coast from Libreville. As we mounted the hill through the rows of neat bamboo huts belonging to the negroes, the chapel doors opened after service. We were introduced to some of the congregation and had a dozen black hands to shake. What a contrast between these clean and decently clothed people and the blacks that we had seen in the seaports, the only kind of native we had met up to now ! Even the faces are not the same. These had a free and yet modest look in them that cleared from my mind the haunting vision of sullen and unwilling subjection, mixed with insolence, which had hitherto looked at me out of the eyes of so many negroes.

From Libreville to Cape Lopez it is only an eight hours' run. When, early on Monday, April 14th, we came in sight of the harbour, an anxiety seized me which I had felt before occasionally during the last week or so. The custom house and the duties! During the latter part of the voyage all sorts of tales had been told at meal times about the colonial duties. "Ten per cent. on the value of all you bring you'll have to fork out!" said an old African. "And whether the things are new or old doesn't matter in the least!" added another. However, the customs officer was fairly gracious to us. Perhaps the anxious faces we showed, as we laid before him the list of the things in our seventy cases, toned him down to a gentler mood, and we returned to the ship with a delightful feeling of relief, to sleep in it for the last time. But it was an uncomfortable night : cargo was being unloaded and coal taken in, till the negroes at the cranes could no longer stand for weariness.

*

*   *

Early on Tuesday we transferred to the *Alembe*, which, being a river boat, was built broad and shallow, and its two paddle-wheels were side by side at the stern, where they are safe from wandering tree trunks. It took up only the passengers and their personal luggage, being already full of cargo. Our cases were to follow in the next boat a fortnight later. We started at 9 a.m., so as to pass safely at high tide over the sandbanks which block the mouth of the Ogowe, and a few passengers who had stayed on shore too long were left behind. They overtook us, however, later on in a motor boat.

River and forest . . . ! Who can really describe the first impression they make ? We seemed to be dreaming ! Pictures of antediluvian scenery which elsewhere had seemed to be merely the creation of fancy, are now seen in real life. It is impossible to say where the river ends and the land begins, for a mighty network of roots, clothed with bright-flowering creepers, projects right into the water. Clumps of palms and palm trees, ordinary trees spreading out widely with green boughs and huge leaves, single trees of the pine family shooting up to a towering height in between them, wide fields of papyrus clumps as tall as a man, with big fan-like leaves, and amid all this luxuriant greenery the rotting stems of dead giants shooting up to heaven. . . . In every gap in the forest a water mirror meets the eye ; at every bend in the river a new tributary shows itself. A heron flies heavily up and then settles on a dead tree trunk ; white birds and blue birds skim over the water, and high in air a pair of ospreys circle. Then—yes, there can be no mistake about it !—from the branch of a palm there hang and swing—two monkey tails ! Now the owners of the tails are visible. We are really in Africa !

So it goes on hour by hour. Each new corner, each new bend, is like the last. Always the same forest and the same yellow water. The impression which nature makes on us is immeasurably deepened by the constant and monotonous repetition. You shut your eyes for an hour, and when you open them you see exactly what you saw before. The Ogowe is not a river but a river system, three or four branches, each as big as the Rhine, twisting themselves together, and in between are lakes big and little. How the black pilot finds his way correctly through this maze of watercourses is a riddle to me. With the spokes of the great wheel in his hand he guides the ship, without any map before him, from the main stream into a narrow side channel, from this into the lake, and from the lake back into the main stream ; and so again and again. But he has worked up and down this stretch of water for sixteen years, and can find his way along even by moonlight !

The current in the lower part of the river is sluggish, but it is very different higher up, though it nowhere becomes as strong as that of the Rhine. Invisible sandbanks and tree trunks floating just below the surface demand very cautious navigation, and the boat's average speed is not more than eight miles an hour.

After a long run we stop at a small negro village, where, stacked on the river bank, are several hundred logs of wood, such as bakers often use, and we lie to in order to ship them, as wood is the fuel used for the engines. A plank is put out to the bank ; the negroes form line and carry the logs on board. On the deck stands another negro with a paper, and as soon as ten logs have passed, another on the plank calls to him in musical tones, " Put a one." When the hundredth log comes, the call, in the same pleasant tone, is, " Put a cross." The price is from four to five francs a hundred, which is rather high when one considers that the logs are all windfalls and only have to be collected.

The captain abuses the village elder for not having had logs enough ready. The latter excuses himself with pathetic words and gestures. At last they come to an agreement that he shall be paid in spirits instead of in cash, because he thinks that the whites get their liquor cheaper than the blacks do, so that he will make a better bargain. . . . Every litre of alcohol pays two francs duty on coming into the colony, and I pay for the absolute alcohol which I use for medical purposes the same duty as is paid on the ordinary liquor for drinking.

Now the voyage continues. On the banks are the ruins of abandoned huts. " When I came out here fifteen years ago," said a trader who stood near me, " these places were all flourishing villages." " And why are they so no longer ? " I asked. He shrugged his shoulders and said in a low voice, " L'alcohol. . . ."

A little after sunset we lay to opposite a store, and two hours were spent in shipping 3,000 logs. " If we had stopped here in daylight," said the merchant to me, " all the negro passengers " (there were about sixty of them) " would have gone ashore and bought spirits. Most of the money that the timber trade brings into the country is converted into rum. I have travelled about in the colonies a great deal, and can say that rum is the great enemy of every form of civilisation."

Thus with the ennobling impressions that nature makes are mingled pain and fear ; with the darkness of the first evening on the Ogowe there lowers over one the shadow of the misery of Africa. Through the gloaming chimes the monotonous call, " Make a one," " Make a cross " ; and I feel more convinced than ever that this land needs to help it men who will never let themselves be discouraged.

With the help of the moon we are able to go further. Now we see the forest like a gigantic border on the river bank ; now we seem to graze its dark wall, from which there streams out a heat that is almost unendurable. The starlight lies gently on the water ; in the distance there is summer lightning. Soon after midnight the

vessel is anchored in a quiet bay, and the passengers
creep into their mosquito nets. Many sleep in the
cabins ; others on the couches along the walls of the
dining saloon, under which are stored the mail sacks.

About 5 a.m. the engines are set in motion again.
We have now covered nearly 130 miles (200 kilometres),
and the forest is more imposing than further downstream. In the distance appears a hill with red roofs
upon it : the mission station of N'Gômô ; and the two
hours spent in shipping logs gives us time to see the
station and its sawmill.

Five hours later the slopes of Lambarene come in
sight, and the steamer sounds its syren, though it will
take another half hour to reach the village. But the
inhabitants of the widely scattered stores must be
warned in good time, so that they can bring their
canoes to the landing stage and take possession of the
goods that we have brought for them.

The Lambarene mission station is an hour further
on by canoe, so that no one could be at the landing
stage to greet us, but while the cargo was being unloaded
I suddenly saw a long, narrow canoe, rowed by merrily
singing boys, shoot round the ship, and so fast, indeed,
that the white man in the stern had only just time to
throw himself backwards and save his head from
contact with the ship's cable. It is Mr. Christol, with
the lower class of the boys' school, and behind them
comes another boat with Mr. Ellenberger, rowed by
the upper class. The boys had made it a race, and the
younger ones had won ; perhaps, however, because
they were given the lighter boat. They were, therefore,
allowed to convey the doctor and his wife ; the others
took the luggage aboard. What charming young

faces ! One little man walked solemnly about, carrying my heavy rifle.

The canoe journey we found at first anything but comfortable. These vessels are only tree trunks hollowed out and are therefore both flat and narrow, so that their equilibrium is very easily disturbed. Moreover, the rowers do not sit, but stand, which, again, does not contribute to their stability. With a long, narrow paddle, which is held freely in the hands, the crew strike the water, singing also so as to keep in time with each other, and a single awkward movement of one of the rowers may upset the canoe. However, in half an hour's time we had overcome our anxiety, and enjoyed the trip thoroughly. The steamer was by now again on its way upstream, and the boys raced it, with such eagerness, too, that they nearly ran into another canoe with three old negresses in it.

In half an hour's time we leave the main stream for a branch one, the singing still going on as merrily as ever, and we can see some white spots on a hill that is flooded with light from the setting sun : the houses of the mission station ! The nearer we get, the louder is the singing, and, after crossing a stream which gusts of wind make rather rough, the canoe glides into a quiet little bay.

First there are a dozen black hands to shake, but that seems now quite natural. Then, Mrs. Christol, Miss Humbert, the schoolmistress, and Mr. Kast, the manual worker, conduct us to our little house, which the children have hastily decorated with palms and flowers. Built of wood, the house stands on some forty iron piles, which raise it about 20 inches from the ground, and a verandah runs all round its four small rooms. The

view is entrancing : below us is the stream, which here
and there widens into a lake ; all round is forest, but
in the distance can be seen a stretch of the main stream,
and the background is a range of blue hills.

We have scarcely time to unpack the things we need
at once when night comes on, as it does here always
just after six. Then the bell summons the children to
prayers in the schoolroom, and a host of crickets begin
to chirp, making a sort of accompaniment to the hymn,
the sound of which floats over to us, while I sit on a box
and listen, deeply moved. But there comes an ugly
shadow creeping down the wall ; I look up, startled,
and see a huge spider, much bigger than the finest I
had ever seen in Europe. An exciting hunt, and the
creature is done for.

After supper with the Christols the school children
appear in front of the verandah, which has been
decorated with paper lanterns, and sing in two parts
to the tune of a Swiss *Volkslied* some verses composed
by Mr. Ellenberger in honour of the doctor's arrival.
Then we are escorted by a squad of lantern-bearers up
the path to our house, but before we can think of retiring
to rest we have to undertake a battle with spiders and
flying cockroaches, who seem to regard as their own
domain the house which has been so long uninhabited.

At six o'clock next morning the bell rings ; the hymn
sung by the children in the schoolroom is soon heard,
and we prepare to begin our new work in our new home.

CHAPTER III

FIRST IMPRESSIONS AND EXPERIENCES

LAMBARENE, *July*, 1913.

STRICT orders had been widely published that only the most serious cases were to be brought to the doctor for the first three weeks, so that he might have time to settle in, but, naturally, not much attention was paid to them. Sick people turned up at every hour of the day, but practical work was very difficult, as, first of all, I had to rely on any interpreter who might be picked up on the road, and, secondly, I had no drugs, instruments, or bandages except what I had brought in my trunk.

A year before my arrival a black teacher in the mission school at Samkita, N'Zeng by name, had offered his services as interpreter and doctor's assistant, and I had sent word to him to come to Lambarene immediately on my arrival, but he did not come because in his native village, sixty miles away, he had to carry through a legal dispute over a will. At last I had to send a canoe with a message that he must come at once, and he promised to do so, but week after week went by and still he did not arrive. Then Mr. Ellenberger said to me with a smile: " Doctor, your education has begun. You are finding out for the first time what every day will prove to you more conclusively, how impossible it is to rely upon the blacks."

During the night of April 26th we heard the whistle of the steamer and soon learnt that our cases had been unloaded at the Catholic mission station, which is on the river bank, the captain having refused to venture on the, to him, unknown water of our branch stream. Fortunately, however, Mr. Champel and Mr. Pelot, the industrial missionaries from N'Gômô, had come to Lambarene, with ten of their native labourers, to help us.   I was extremely anxious about the conveyance of my piano with pedal attachment, built for the tropics, which the Bach Society of Paris had given me, in recognition of many years' service as their organist, so that I might keep myself in practice even in Africa. It seemed to me impossible that such a piano, in its heavy zinc-lined case, could be carried in a hollowed-out tree trunk, and yet there are no other boats here ! One store, however, possessed a canoe, hewn out of a gigantic tree, which could carry up to three tons weight, and this they lent me. It would have carried five pianos !

Soon, by dint of hard work, we got our seventy cases across, and to get them up the hill from the river bank every sound set of limbs in the station came to help, the school children working as zealously as any one. It was amusing to see how a case suddenly got a crowd of black legs underneath it and two rows of woolly heads apparently growing out of its sides, and how, amid shouting and shrieking, it thus crept up the hill ! In three days everything had been carried up, and the N'Gômô helpers were able to go home. We hardly knew how to thank them enough, for without their help we could not possibly have managed the job.

Unpacking was a trial, for it was difficult to dispose

of the various articles. I had been promised a corrugated-iron building as a hospital, but it was impossible to get its framework erected, as there were no labourers to be had. For several months the timber trade had been very good, and the traders paid the labourers wages with which the Mission could not compete. In order, however, that I might have ready at hand, at any rate, the most necessary drugs, Mr. Kast, the industrial missionary, fixed some shelves in my sitting-room, the wood for which he had himself cut and planed. One must be in Africa to understand what a boon some shelves on the wall are!

That I had no place in which to examine and treat the sick worried me much. Into my own room I could not take them for fear of infection. One arranges at once in Africa (so the missionaries impressed on me from the beginning) that the blacks shall be in the white people's quarters as little as possible. This is a necessary part of one's care for oneself. So I treated and bandaged the sick in the open air before the house, and when the usual evening storm came on, everything had to be hastily carried into the verandah. Treating patients in the sun was, moreover, very fatiguing.

*

*   *

Under the pressure of this discomfort I decided to promote to the rank of hospital the building which my predecessor in the house, Mr. Morel, the missionary, had used as a fowlhouse. I got some shelves fixed on the walls, installed an old camp-bed, and covered the worst of the dirt with whitewash, feeling myself more than fortunate. It was, indeed, horribly close in the little windowless room, and the bad state of the roof made it necessary to wear my sun-helmet all day, but when the storm came on I did not have to move every-thing under cover.   I felt proud the first time I heard the rain rattling on the roof, and it seemed incredible that I could go quietly on with my bandaging.

At the same time I discovered an interpreter and assistant.   Amongst my patients there turned up a very intelligent-looking native, who spoke French remarkably well, and said he was a cook by trade but had had to give up that kind of work as it disagreed with his health.   I asked him to come to us tem-porarily, as we could not find a cook, and at the same time to help me as interpreter and surgical assistant. His name was Joseph, and he proved extremely handy. It was hardly surprising that, as he had acquired his knowledge of anatomy in the kitchen, he should, as a matter of habit, use kitchen terms in the surgery : " This man's right leg of mutton (gigot) hurts him." " This woman has a pain in her upper left cutlet, and in her loin ! "   At the end of May N'Zeng arrived, the man whom I had written to engage beforehand, but as he did not seem to be very reliable, I kept Joseph on. Joseph is a Galoa, N'Zeng a Pahouin.

Work was now fairly well started.   My wife had charge of the instruments and made the necessary preparations for the surgical operations, at which she served as assistant, and she also looked after the bandages and the washing of the linen.   Consultations begin about 8.30, the patients waiting in the shade of my house in front of the fowlhouse, which is my surgery, and every morning one of the assistants reads out—

THE DOCTOR'S STANDING ORDERS.

1. Spitting near the doctor's house is strictly forbidden.

2. Those who are waiting must not talk to each other loudly.

3. Patients and their friends must bring with them food enough for one day, as they cannot all be treated early in the day.

4. Any one who spends the night on the station without the doctor's permission will be sent away without any medicine. (It happened not infrequently that patients from a distance crowded into the schoolboys' dormitory turned them out, and took their places.)

5. All bottles and tin boxes in which medicines are given must be returned.

6. In the middle of the month, when the steamer has gone up the river, none but urgent cases can be seen till the steamer has gone down again, as the doctor is then writing to Europe to get more of his valuable medicines. (The steamer brings the mail from Europe about the middle of the month, and on its return takes our letters down to the coast.)

These six commandments are read out every day very carefully in the dialects of both the Galoas and the Pahouins, so that no long discussion can arise afterwards. Those present accompany each sentence with a nod, which indicates that they understand, and at the finish comes a request that the doctor's words shall be made known in all the villages, both on the river and on the lakes.

At 12.30 the assistant announces : " The doctor is going to have his lunch." More nods to show that they understand, and the patients scatter to eat their own bananas in the shade. At 2 p.m. we return, but at

6 p.m. there are often some who have not yet been seen, and they have to be put off till the next day. To treat them by lamplight cannot be thought of because of the mosquitoes and the risk of fever infection.

Each patient is given, on leaving, a round piece of cardboard on a string of fibre, on which is the number under which his name, his complaint, and the medicines given him are recorded in my register, so that if he comes back I have only to turn to the page to learn all about the case, and be spared a time-wasting second diagnosis. The register records also all the bottles, boxes, bandages, etc., which were given ; only with this means of control is it possible to demand the return of these things, which in about half the cases we do get back. How valuable bottles and boxes are away from the civilised world only he can rightly estimate who has had to get medicines ready in the primeval forest for patients to take home with them ! The atmosphere is so damp here that medicines, which in Europe can be wrapped in paper or distributed in cardboard boxes, can only be kept in good condition in a corked bottle or in a tin box which closes perfectly. I had not taken sufficient account of this, and I found myself in such difficulty about it that I had to fall out with patients who said they had forgotten or lost a tin box. My friends in Europe were entreated by every post to collect from their acquaintances bottles big and little, glass tubes with corks, and tin boxes of all sorts and sizes. How I look forward to the day when I shall have a sufficient supply of such things !

The round cardboard ticket with the number on it most of the patients wear round their neck, together with

the metal one which shows that they have paid their
five franc poll tax for the current year. It is seldom
lost or forgotten, and many of them, especially among
the Pahouins, regard it as a kind of fetish.

My name among the natives in Galoa is " Oganga,"
i.e., fetishman. They have no other name for a doctor,
as those of their own tribesmen who practise the healing art are all fetishmen. My patients take it to be
only logical that the man who can heal disease should
also have the power of producing it, and that even at a
distance. To me it is striking that I should have the
reputation of being such a good creature and yet, at
the same time, such a dangerous one ! That the diseases have some natural cause never occurs to my
patients : they attribute them to evil spirits, to mali-
cious human magic, or to " the worm," which is their
imaginary embodiment of pain of every sort. When
they are asked to describe their symptoms, they talk
about the worm, telling how he was first in their legs,
then got into their head, and from there made his way
to their heart ; how he then visited their lungs, and
finally settled in their stomach. All medicines have
to be directed to expelling him. If I quiet a colic
with tincture of opium, the patient comes next day
beaming with joy and tells me the worm has been driven
out of his body but is now settled in his head and is
devouring his brain : will I please give him something
to banish the worm from his head too ?

A great deal of time is lost trying to make them
understand how the medicines are to be taken. Over
and over again the interpreter tells them, and they
repeat it after him ; it is written, also, on the bottle
or box, so that they can hear the directions again from

any one in their village who can read, but in the end I am never sure that they do not empty the bottle at one go, and eat the ointment, and rub the powders into their skin. I get, on the average, from thirty to forty people a day to treat, and the chief complaints are skin diseases of various sorts, malaria, the sleeping sickness, leprosy, elephantiasis, heart complaints, suppurating injuries to the bones (osteomyelitis), and tropical dysentery. To stop the discharge from the sores the natives cover the place with powder made from the bark of a certain tree. This hardens gradually into a paste which hinders the escape of the pus and, of course, makes the case much worse.

From the list of the complaints which come oftenest to be treated the itch (scabies) must not be omitted. It causes the blacks very great distress, and I have had patients who had not slept for weeks because they had been so tortured by the itching ; many had scratched their whole body till the blood came, so that there were festering sores to treat as well as scabies. The treatment is very simple. The patient first washes in the river, and is then rubbed all over, however tall he is, with an ointment compounded of flower of sulphur (*sulphur depuratum*), crude palm oil, remains of oil from sardine tins, and soft soap. In a tin which once contained sterilised milk he receives a quantity of this ointment with which to give himself at home two more rubbings. The success of this is wonderful, the itching ceasing to worry on the second day, and this ointment has in a very few weeks made me famous far and wide.

The natives have great confidence in the white man's medicine, a result which is partly, at any rate, due to the self-sacrificing spirit and the wise understanding with which they have been treated for a generation here on the Ogowe. In this connection I may specially mention Mrs. Lantz, of Talagouga, a native of Alsace, who died in 1906, and Mr. Robert, of N'Gômô, a Swiss, who is now lying seriously ill in Europe.

My work is rendered much harder by the fact that I can keep so few medicines in the fowlhouse. For almost every patient I have to cross the court to my dispensary, there to weigh out or to prepare the medicine needed, which is very fatiguing and wastes much time. When will the iron building for the hospital be seriously taken in hand ? Will it be ready before the autumn rainy season begins ? What shall I do if it is not ready ? In the hot season I shall not be able to work in the fowlhouse.

I am worried, too, by the fact that I have hardly any medicines left, for my *clientèle* is much more numerous than I had expected. By the June mail I sent off an extensive order, but the things will not be here for three or four months, and my quinine, anti-pyrin, bromide of potassium, salol, and dermatol are almost exhausted.

Yet what do all these disagreeables count for compared with the joy of being here, working and helping ? However limited one's means are, how much one can do with them ! Just to see the joy of those who are plagued with sores, when these have been cleanly bandaged up and they no longer have to drag their poor, bleeding feet through the mud, makes it worth while to work here. How I should like all my helpers to be able to see on Mondays and Thursdays—the days set apart for the bandaging of sores—the freshly bandaged patients walking or being carried down the

hill, or that they could have watched the eloquent
gestures with which an old woman with heart complaint
described how, thanks to digitalis, she could once more
breathe and sleep, because the medicine had made
" the worm " crawl right away down to her feet !

As I look back over the work of two months and a
half, I can only say that a doctor is needed, terribly
needed, here ; that for a huge distance round the
natives avail themselves of his help, and that with
comparatively small means he can accomplish a quite
disproportionate amount of good.   The need is terrible.
" Here, among us, everybody is ill," said a young man
to me a few days ago.   " Our country devours its own
children," was the remark of an old chief.

CHAPTER IV

JULY, 1913—JANUARY, 1914

THE Lambarene mission station is built on hills, the one which lies farthest upstream having on its summit the buildings of the boys' school, and on the side which slopes down to the river the storehouse and the largest of the mission houses. On the middle hill is the doctor's little house, and on the remaining one the girls' school and the other mission house. Some twenty yards beyond the houses is the edge of the forest. We live, then, between the river and the virgin forest, on three hills, which every year have to be secured afresh against the invasion of wild Nature, who is ever trying to get her own back again. All round the houses there are coffee bushes, cocoa trees, lemon trees, orange trees, mandarin trees, mango trees, oil palms, and pawpaw trees. To the negroes its name has always been " Andende." Deeply indebted are we to the first missionaries that they took so much trouble to grow these big trees.

The station is about 650 yards long and 110 to 120 yards across. We measure it again and again in every direction in our evening and Sunday constitutionals, which one seldom or never takes on the paths that lead to the nearest villages. On these

paths the heat is intolerable, for on either side of these
narrow passages rises the forest in an impenetrable
wall nearly 100 feet high, and between these walls not
a breath of air stirs. There is the same absence of
air and movement in Lambarene. One seems to be
living in a prison. If we could only cut down a corner
of the forest which shuts in the lower end of the station
we should get a little of the breeze in the river valley ;
but we have neither the money nor the men for such
an attack on the trees. The only relief we have is that
in the dry season the river sandbanks are exposed, and
we can take our exercise upon them and enjoy the
breeze which blows upstream.

It had been originally intended to put the hospital
buildings on the ridge of high ground on which the
boys' school stands, but as the site was both too far
away and too small, I had arranged with the staff of
the station that I should be given a place for it at the
foot of the hill on which I myself lived, on the side next
the river. This decision had, however, to be confirmed
by the Conference of Missionaries which had been called
to meet at Samkita at the end of July. So I went there
with Mr. Ellenberger and Mr. Christol, to put my case,
and that was my first long journey in a canoe.

* * *

We started one misty morning two hours before day-
break, the two missionaries and myself sitting one
behind the other in long folding chairs in the bow.
The middle of the canoe was filled with our tin boxes,
our folded camp-bedsteads, the mattresses, and with
the bananas which formed the rations of the natives.
Behind these things were the twelve rowers in six

pairs one behind the other; these sang about the destination to which we were bound and about who was on board, weaving in plaintive remarks about having to begin work so early and the hard day's work they had in front of them! Ten to twelve hours was the time usually allowed for the thirty to thirty-five miles upstream to Samkita, but our boat was so heavily laden that it was necessary to allow somewhat longer.

As we swung out from the side channel into the river, day broke, and enabled us to see along the huge sandbank some 350 yards ahead some dark lines moving about in the water. The rowers' song stopped instantly, as if at a word of command. The dark lines were the backs of hippopotami, which were enjoying their morning bath after their regular grazing time on land. The natives are much afraid of them and always give them a wide berth, for their temper is very uncertain, and they have destroyed many a canoe.

There was once a missionary stationed in Lambarene who used to make merry over the timidity of his rowers, and challenge them to go nearer to the great animals. One day, just as he was on the point of bursting into laughter, the canoe was suddenly shot up into the air by a hippopotamus which rose from its dive immediately beneath it, and he and the crew only saved themselves with difficulty. All his baggage was lost. He afterwards had a square patch, with the hole that the creature had made, sawn out of the bottom of the canoe, that he might keep it as a souvenir. This happened some years ago, but the story is told to any white man who asks his crew to row nearer to a hippopotamus.

In the main stream the natives always keep close to the bank where the current is not so strong : there are even stretches of river where one finds a counter-current flowing upstream. And so we creep along, as far as possible in the shade of the overhanging trees. This canoe has no rudder, but the rower nearest the stern guides it in obedience to signals from the one in front, who keeps a sharp lookout for shallows, rocks, and floating tree trunks. The most unpleasant thing on these trips is the way in which the light and heat are reflected from the water. One feels as if from the shimmering mirror one were being pierced with arrows of fire. To quench our thirst we had some magnificent pineapples, three for each of us.

Sunrise brought the tsetse fly, which is active only by day, and compared with which the worst mosquito is a comparatively harmless creature.* It is about half as large again as our ordinary house fly, which it resembles in appearance, only its wings, when closed, do not lie parallel to each other but overlap like the blades of a pair of scissors. To get blood it can pierce the thickest cloth, but it is extremely cautious and artful, and evades cleverly all blows of the hands. The moment it feels that the body on which it has settled makes the slightest movement, it flies off and hides itself on the side of the boat. Its flight is inaudible and a small fly-whisk is the only means of protecting oneself to some extent from it. Its habit of caution makes it avoid settling on any light-coloured object, on which it would be easily detected : hence white clothes are the best protection against it. This state-ment I found fully confirmed during this trip, for two of us wore white, and one yellow clothes. The two of

---

* The *Glossina palpalis*, which conveys the germs of the sleeping sickness, belongs, as is well known, to the Tsetse family.

us hardly ever had a fly upon us : our companion had to endure continual annoyance, but the blacks were the worst sufferers.

At mid-day we stopped at a native village, and while we ate the provisions we had brought with us, our crew roasted their bananas. I wished that after such hard work they could have had some more substantial food. It was very late in the evening before we reached our destination.

With the conference, which sat for a whole week, I was strongly impressed. I felt it inspiring to be working with men who for years had practised such renunciation in order to devote themselves to the service of the natives, and I enjoyed thoroughly the refreshing atmosphere of love and good-will. My proposal had a most friendly reception : it was decided that the iron shed and the other hospital buildings should be erected on the place I had in view, and the mission gave me £80 (4,000 fr.) towards the cost of building.

On our return journey we crossed the river twice in order to avoid groups of hippopotami, one of which came up only fifty yards away. Darkness had already come on when we reached our side channel, and for a whole hour we had to pick our way between sandbanks, the crew having now and again to jump out and pull or push the canoe forward. At last we got into deep water : the song of the crew deepened into a roar, and soon we saw lights moving, which advanced in zigzag lines down to a lower level and there came to a halt together. It was the ladies of Lambarene and the negro women who had come to meet the returning travellers at the landing place. The canoe cuts through the water with a whish, and with a last spurt is carried high up the beach. The

rowers give a yell of triumph, while black hands without
number reach out for the boxes, the beds, the bags,
and the vegetables we have brought from Samkita.
" This is Mr. Christol's."   " This is Mr. Ellenberger's."
" This is the Doctor's."   " Two of you to that ; it's too
heavy for one ! "   " Don't drop it ! "   " Be careful with
the guns ! "   " Wait : not here ; put it over there ! "
and so on.   At last the whole cargo has been distributed
to the right places, and we go joyfully up the hill.

Our immediate task now was to level the site for the
hospital by the removal of several cubic metres of soil.
After a world of trouble the Mission managed to secure
four or five labourers whose laziness was perfectly
magnificent, till my patience at last gave way.   A
timber merchant whom we knew, Mr. Rapp, had just
arrived with a working party in order to examine the
neighbouring forest, in which he wanted to secure a
concession, and he was staying at the Catholic mission
in order to clear off his correspondence.   At my request
he put eight of his sturdy carriers at my disposal.   I
promised them handsome pay and took a spade in hand
myself, while the black foreman lay in the shade of a
tree and occasionally threw us an encouraging word.
With two days of steady work we had got the soil
cleared away and the spot levelled.   The labourers
went off with their pay, but on the way back, I regret
to say, they stopped at a store and, in spite of my
warnings, turned it all into spirits.   They reached
home in the middle of the night, blind drunk, and the
next day were fit for nothing.   But we were now in a
position to begin building the hospital.

Joseph and I were now doing all the work without help. N'Zeng went off to his village on leave in August, and, as he did not return at the time agreed on, he was discharged. Joseph gets 70 francs (£2 16s.) a month, though as a cook at Cape Lopez he used to get 120 (£4 16s.). He finds it hard that work demanding some education should be worse paid than the common kinds.

The number of people with heart complaints astonishes me more and more. They, on the other hand, are astonished that I know all about their trouble as soon as I have examined them with the stethoscope. " Now I believe we've got a real doctor ! " said an old woman to Joseph not long ago. " He knows that I can often hardly breathe at night, and that I often have swollen feet, yet I've never told him a word about it and he has never even looked at my feet." I cannot help saying to myself that there is something really glorious in the means which modern medicine has for treating the heart. I give digitalis according to the new French method (daily doses of a tenth of a milligram of digitalin continued for weeks and months) and am more than pleased with the results obtained. It must be said that it is easier to treat heart disease here than it is in Europe, for when patients are told that they must rest and keep quiet for weeks, they are never obliged to object that they will lose their wages and perhaps their work. They simply live at home and "recruit," and their family, in the widest sense of that word, supports them.

Mental complaints are relatively rarer here than in Europe, though I have already seen some half-dozen such. They are a great worry as I do not know how to

dispose of them. If they are allowed to remain on the
station they disturb us with their cries all the night
through, and I have to get up again and again to
quieten them with a subcutaneous injection. I can
look back on several terrible nights which resulted in
my feeling tired for many a day afterwards. The difficulty can be surmounted in the dry season, for then I
can make the mental patients and their friends camp
out on a sandbank about 600 yards away, although
getting across to see them twice a day consumes a great
deal both of time and of energy.

The condition of these poor creatures out here is
dreadful. The natives do not know how to protect
themselves from them. Confinement is impossible, as
they can at any time break out of a bamboo hut. They
are therefore bound with cords of bast, but that only
makes their condition worse, and the final result almost
always is that they are somehow or other got rid of.
One of the Samkita missionaries told me once that a
couple of years before, while sitting one Sunday in his
house, he had heard loud cries in a neighbouring village.
He got up and started off to see what was the matter,
but met a native who told him it was only that some
children were having the sand flies cut out from their
feet ; he need not worry, but might go home again.
He did so, but learnt the next day that one of the villagers, who had become insane, had been bound hand
and foot and thrown into the water.

My first contact with a mentally-diseased native
happened at night. I was knocked up and taken to a
palm tree to which an elderly woman was bound.
Around a fire in front of her sat the whole of her family,
and behind them was the black forest wall. It was a

glorious African night and the shimmering glow of the starry sky lighted up the scene. I ordered them to set her free, which they did, but with timidity and hesitation. The woman was no sooner free than she sprang at me in order to seize my lamp and throw it away. The natives fled with shrieks in every direction and would not come any nearer, even when the woman, whose hand I had seized, sank quietly to the ground as I told her, and offered me her arm for an injection of morphia and scopolamin. A few moments later she followed me to a hut, where, in a short time, she went to sleep. The case was one of an attack of recurrent maniacal disturbance, and in a fortnight she was well again, at least for a time. In consequence of this the report spread that the doctor was a great magician and could cure all mental diseases.

Unfortunately, I was soon to learn that there are forms of maniacal disturbance here with which our drugs can do little or nothing. The second case was an old man, and he, too, was brought with hands and feet bound. The ropes had cut deeply into his flesh, and hands and feet alike were covered with blood and sores. I was amazed at the small effect produced by the strongest doses of morphia, scopolamin, chloral hydrate, and bromide of potassium. On the second day Joseph said to me : " Doctor, believe me, the man is out of his mind because he has been poisoned. You will make nothing of him ; he will get weaker and wilder, and at last he will die." And Joseph was right ; in a fortnight the man was dead. From one of the Catholic fathers I learnt that he had robbed some women, and, therefore, had been followed up and poisoned by their relatives.

A similar case I was able to study from the beginning.

One Sunday evening there arrived in a canoe a woman who was writhing with cramp. I thought at first that it was simple hysteria, but the next day maniacal disturbance supervened, and during the night she began to rave and shriek. On her, too, the narcotics had hardly any effect, and her strength rapidly diminished. The natives surmised that she had been poisoned, and whether they were right or not I am not in a position to decide.

From all I hear it must be true that poison is much used in these parts, and further south that is still oftener the case : the tribes between the Ogowe and the Congo are notorious in this respect. At the same time there are, among the natives, many inexplicable cases of sudden death which are quite unjustifiably regarded as the result of poison.

Anyhow, there must be many plants the juices of which have a peculiarly stimulating effect on the system. I have been assured by trustworthy persons that there are certain leaves and roots which enable men to row for a whole day without experiencing either hunger, thirst, or fatigue, and to display at the same time an increasingly boisterous merriment. I hope in time to learn something more definite about these " medicines, but it is always difficult to do so, because the knowledge about them is kept a strict secret. Any one who is suspected of betraying anything about them, and, above all, if it is to a white man, may count with certainty on being poisoned.

That the medicine men employ poison to maintain their authority I learnt in a peculiar way through Joseph. About the middle of the dry season his village went off to a sandbank about three hours

upstream from here, on a fishing expedition. These
fishing days are not unlike the Old Testament harvest
festivals, when the people " rejoiced before Yahweh."
Old and young live together for a fortnight in " booths "
made with branches of trees and eat at every meal
fresh fish, boiled, baked, or stewed. Whatever is not
consumed is dried and smoked, and if all goes well, a
village may take home with it as many as ten thousand
fish. As Joseph's eyes nearly start from their sockets
whenever the conversation turns on fish, I proposed
to allow him to go out with his village for the first
afternoon, and asked him to take a small tub in which
to bring back a few fishes for the doctor. He showed,
however, no enthusiasm at the prospect, and a few
questions put me in possession of the reason. On
the first day there is no fishing done, but the place
is blessed. The " elders " pour rum and throw
tobacco leaves into the water to put the evil spirits
into a good humour, so that they may let the fish be
caught in the nets and may injure no one. These
ceremonies were once omitted several years ago, but
the following year an old woman wrapped herself up
in a net and let herself be drowned. " But—why ?
Most of you are Christians ! " I exclaimed ; " you
don't believe in these things ! " " Certainly not," he
replied, " but any one who spoke against them or even
allowed himself to smile while the rum and tobacco
were being offered, would assuredly be poisoned sooner
or later. The medicine men never forgive, and they
live among us without any one knowing who they are."
So he stayed at home the first day, but I allowed him
to go some days later.

Besides the fear of poison there is also their dread of the supernatural power for evil which one man can exert over another, for the natives here believe that there are means of acquiring such powers. Whoever has the right fetish can do anything ; he will always be successful when hunting, and he can bring bad luck, sickness, and death on any one whom he wishes to injure. Europeans will never be able to understand how terrible is the life of the poor creatures who pass their days in continual fear of the fetishes which can be used against them. Only those who have seen this misery at close quarters will understand that it is a simple human duty to bring to these primitive peoples a new view of the world which can free them from these torturing superstitions. In this matter the greatest sceptic, did he find himself out here, would prove a real helper of mission work.

What is fetishism ? It is something born of the fears of primitive man. Primitive man wants to possess some charm to protect him from the evil spirits in nature and from those of the dead, as well as from the power for evil of his fellow men, and this protecting power he attributes to certain objects which he carries about with him. He does not worship his fetish, but regards it as a little bit of property which cannot but be of service to him through its supernatural powers.

What makes a fetish ? That which is unknown is supposed to have magical power. A fetish is composed of a number of little objects which fill a small bag, a buffalo horn, or a box ; the things most commonly used are red feathers, small parcels of red earth, leopard's claws and teeth, and . . . bells from Europe ! Bells of an old-fashioned shape which date from the barter transactions of the eighteenth century ! Opposite the mission station a negro has laid out a small cocoa plantation, and the fetish which is expected to protect it hangs on a tree in a corked bottle. Nowadays valuable fetishes are enclosed in tin boxes, so that they may not be damaged by termites, from whose ravages a wooden box gives no permanent protection.

There are big fetishes and little ones. A big one usually includes a piece of human skull, but it must be from the skull of some one who was killed expressly to provide the fetish. Last summer at a short distance below the station an elderly man was killed in a canoe. The murderer was discovered, and it is considered to have been proved that he committed the crime in order to secure a fetish by means of which he hoped to ensure the fulfilment of their contracts by people who owed him goods and money !

A few weeks later my wife and I took a walk one Sunday through the forest to Lake Degele, which is about two hours distant. In the village in which we took a mid-day rest the people had nothing to eat because for several days the women had been afraid to go out to the banana field. It had become known that several men were prowling about the neighbourhood who wanted to kill some one in order to obtain a fetish. The women of Lambarene asserted that these men had also been seen near one of our wells, and the whole district was in a state of excitement for several weeks.

I am myself the possessor of a fetish. The most important objects in it are two fragments of a human skull, of a longish oval shape and dyed with some sort of red colouring matter ; they seem to me to be from

CARL A. RUDISILL
LIBRARY
LENOIR RHYNE COLLEGE

the parietal bones.   The owner was ill for many months, and his wife also, both suffering tortures from sleeplessness.   Several times, however, the man heard in a dream a voice which revealed to him that they could only get well if they took the family fetish he had inherited to Mr. Haug, the missionary in N'Gômô, and followed Mr. Haug's orders.   Mr. Haug referred him to me, and made me a present of the fetish.   The man and his wife stayed with me several weeks for treatment, and were discharged with their health very much improved.

The belief that magical power dwells in human skulls which have been obtained expressly for this purpose, must be a quite primitive one.   I saw not long ago in a medical periodical the assertion that the supposed cases of trephining which have often been recognised during the excavation and examination of prehistoric graves were by no means attempts at treatment of tumours on the brain or similar growths, as had been assumed, but were simply operations for the securing of fetish objects.   The author of the article is probably right.*

*

*   *

In the first nine months of my work here I have had close on two thousand patients to examine, and I can affirm that most European diseases are represented here ;   I even had a child with whooping-cough.

* In Keith's " Antiquity of Man " (Williams and Norgate, 1915), p. 21, is a picture of a prehistoric skull in which there is a hole made by trephining, as is shown by the fact that the edges are bevelled off.   The condition of the bone shows further that the wound had healed prior to death.

Cancer, however, and appendicitis I have never seen. Apparently they have not yet reached the negroes of Equatorial Africa. On the other hand, chills play a great part here. At the beginning of the dry season there is as much sneezing and coughing in the church at Lambarene as there is in England at a midnight service on New Year's Eve. Many children die of unrecognised pleurisy.

In the dry season the nights are fresher and colder than at other times, and as the negroes have no bed clothes they get so cold in their huts that they cannot sleep, even though according to European standards the temperature is still fairly high. On cold nights the thermometer shows at least 68° F., but the damp of the atmosphere, which makes people sweat continually by day, makes them thereby so sensitive that they shiver and freeze by night. White people, too, suffer continually from chills and colds in the head, and there is much truth in a sentence I came across in a book on tropical medicine, though it seemed at the time rather paradoxical : " Where the sun is hot, one must be more careful than elsewhere to avoid chills." Especially fatal to the natives is the camp life on the sandbanks when they are out on their summer fishing expeditions. Most of the old folk die of pneumonia which they have caught on these occasions.

Rheumatism is commoner here than in Europe, and I not infrequently come across cases of gout, though the sufferers cannot be said to bring it on by an epicurean diet. That they eat too much flesh food cannot possibly be alleged, as except for the fish-days in summer they live almost exclusively on bananas and manioc.

That I should have to treat chronic nicotine poisoning
out here I should never have believed. At first I
could not tell what to think of acute constipation which
was accompanied by nervous disturbances and only
made worse by aperients, but while treating a black
Government official who was suffering severely I came
to see clearly, through observation and questioning,
that the misuse of tobacco lay at the root of it. The
man soon got well and the case was much talked of,
as he had been a sufferer for years and had become
almost incapable of work. From that time, whenever
a case of severe constipation came to me, I asked at
once : " How many pipes a day do you smoke ? " and
I recognised in a few weeks what mischief nicotine
produces here. It is among the women that cases of
nicotine poisoning are most frequent. Joseph explained
to me that the natives suffer much from insomnia, and
then smoke all through the night in order to stupefy
themselves.

Tobacco comes here from America in the form of
leaves, seven of which form a head (*tête de tabac*). It
is a plant which is frightfully common and also frightfully strong (much stronger than that which is smoked
by white people), and it largely takes the place of small
coins : *e.g.*, one leaf, worth about a halfpenny, will buy
two pineapples, and almost all temporary services are
paid for by means of it. If you have to travel, you
take for the purchase of food for the crew, not money,
for that has no value in the forest, but a box of tobacco-
leaves, and to prevent the men from helping themselves
to its valuable contents you make it your seat. A
pipe goes from mouth to mouth during the journey ;
and anybody who wants to travel fast and will promise

his crew an extra two leaves each, is sure to arrive an
hour or two sooner than he otherwise would.

*

*   *

The teeth also give the natives much trouble. Many
of my patients suffer from shrinking of the gums
together with purulent discharges (*pyorrhœa*) caused by
accumulations of tartar. Then, in course of time, all
the teeth get loose and fall out. Strange to say, these
cases get well more quickly here than in Europe, where
the complicated treatment often fails to attain its
object. I have obtained successful results from
regular painting with an alcoholic solution of thymol,
only the patient has to be careful not to swallow any
of the liquid, which is, of course, very poisonous.

It seems to the natives almost incredible that I can
extract teeth which are not yet loose, but they do not
all trust the polished forceps ! A chief who was plagued
with toothache would not submit to their use till he
had gone home again to consult his wives. Presumably
the family decision was unfavourable, as he did not
present himself again. On the other hand, some
request me to take all their teeth out and to get them
new ones from Europe. A few old folk have, through
the missionaries, actually got some double sets, " made
by the white people," and they are now an object of
much envy.

Abdominal tumours are very common here with the
women.

My hope that I should not need to perform any major
operation before the medical ward was ready for use
was disappointed. On August 15th I had to operate
on a case of strangulated hernia which had been brought

in the evening before. The man, whose name was
Aïnda, begged me to operate, for, like all the natives, he
knew well enough the dangers of his condition. There
was, in fact, no time to lose, and the instruments were
brought together as quickly as possible. Mr. Christol
allowed me to use his boys' bedroom as an operating
theatre ; my wife undertook to give the anæsthetic,
and a missionary acted as assistant. Everything went
off better than we could have expected, but I was
almost staggered by the quiet confidence with which the
man placed himself in position on the operating table.

A military doctor from the interior, who is going to
Europe on leave, tells me that he envies me the excellent
assistance I had for my first operation on hernia ! He
himself, he said, had performed his with one native
prisoner handing him the instruments and another
administering the chloroform by guesswork, while each
time they moved the fetters on their legs rattled ; but
his regular assistant was ill and there was no one who
could take his place.

The aseptic precautions were, naturally, far from
perfect, but the patient recovered.

January 10th, 1914. I had scarcely finished writing
the above paragraphs this afternoon when I had to
hurry off to the landing place. Mrs. Faure, the wife
of the missionary at N'Gômô, arrived in a motor boat,
suffering from a severe attack of malaria, and I had
scarcely given her a first intramuscular injection of
quinine when a canoe brought in a young man who
had had his right thigh broken and badly mutilated by
a hippopotamus in Lake Sonange. In other respects,
too, the poor fellow was in a bad condition. He and a
friend had gone out together to fish, but not far from

the landing place of their village a hippopotamus had
come up unexpectedly and hurled their boat into the
air. The friend escaped, but my patient was chased
about in the water by the enraged beast for half an
hour, though he was able at last to get to shore in spite
of his broken thigh. I was afraid there would be
serious blood poisoning, for they had brought him the
twelve hours' canoe journey with his mutilated thigh
wrapped in dirty rags.

I have myself had a meeting with a hippo, but it,
fortunately, ended well. One autumn evening I was
called up to visit a planter, and to get to him we had
to pass a narrow canal about fifty yards long with a
very strong current. On the journey out we saw two
hippos in the distance. For the journey home, which
would be in the dark, for night had fallen, the store
people advised me to make a detour of a couple of
hours so as to avoid the canal and the animals, but the
rowers were so tired that I would not ask them for so
much extra exertion. We had just got to the entrance
of the canal when the two hippos came up from a dive
thirty yards ahead of us, their roar sounding much as if
children were blowing a trumpet into a watering can,
only louder. The crew at once drew in close to the bank,
where the current was least strong, but we advanced
very slowly, foot by foot, the hippos accompanying us,
swimming along the other bank. It was a wonderful,
exciting experience. Some palm tree stems, which had
got fixed in mid-stream, rose out of the water and
swayed about like reeds ; on the bank the forest rose
straight up like a black wall, and an enchanting moonlight illuminated the whole scene. The rowers gasped
with fear and encouraged each other with low calls

E

while the hippos pushed their ugly heads out of the water and glared angrily across at us. In a quarter of an hour we had got out of the canal and were descending the narrow arm of the river, followed by a parting roar from the hippos. I vowed that never in future would I be so scrupulous about adding even two hours to a journey in order to get out of the way of these interesting animals, yet I should be sorry not to be able to look back on those wonderful minutes, uncomfortable though the experience seemed at the time.

*

*   *

Towards evening on November 1st I was again called upon to go to N'Gômô. Mrs. Faure had, without thinking, walked a few yards in the open without anything on her head, and was now prostrate with severe fever and other threatening symptoms. Truly my fellow-traveller on the *Europe* was right when he said that the sun was our great enemy. Here are some further examples :—

A white man, working in a store, was resting after dinner with a ray of sunshine falling on his head through a hole in the roof about the size of a half-crown : the result was high fever with delirium.

Another lost his pith helmet when his boat was upset. As soon as he got on to the boat, which was floating away keel uppermost, he threw himself on his back and, anticipating danger, at once took off his coat and his shirt to protect his head with them. It was too late, however, and he got a bad sunstroke.

The skipper of a small merchant vessel had to make some small repairs to the keel of his craft, which had been drawn up dry on land. While working at them he bent his head so far that the sun shone upon his neck below his helmet. He, too, was for a time at death's door.

Children, however, are less affected than adults. Mrs. Christol's little daughter not long ago ran unobserved out of the house and walked about in the sun for nearly ten minutes without taking any harm. I am now so used to this state of things that I shudder every time I see people represented in illustrated papers as walking about bareheaded in the open air, and I have to reassure myself that even white people can do this with impunity in Europe.

The skipper of the little steamer, who had himself been down with sunstroke, had been kind enough to offer to fetch me to N'Gômô, and my wife went with me to help to nurse the patient. Following the advice of an experienced colonial doctor, I treated the sunstroke as if it were complicated with malaria, and gave intramuscular injections of a strong solution of quinine. It has been proved that sunstroke is especially dangerous to people who are already infected with malaria, and many doctors even assert that quite half the symptoms are to be put down to the malarial attack which is brought on by the sunstroke. A further necessity in such cases, when the patient can take nothing or brings everything up again, is to introduce sufficient fluid into the system to avert such injury to the kidneys as might endanger life. This is effected best with a pint of distilled and sterilised water containing 65 grains ($4\frac{1}{2}$ grams) of the purest kitchen salt, which is introduced under the skin or into a vein in the arm with a cannula.

On our return from N'Gômô we were agreeably surprised to hear that the corrugated iron hospital ward was ready. A fortnight later the internal fitting up was practically finished, and Joseph and I left the fowl-house and settled in, my wife helping us vigorously. I owe hearty thanks for this building to Mr. Kast and Mr. Ottmann, the two practical workers of the Mission ; the former a Swiss, the latter a native of the Argentine. It was a great advantage that we could discuss all details together, and that these two were willing to listen to the considerations, suggested by my medical knowledge. Hence the building, although it is so plain and so small, is extraordinarily convenient : every nook and corner is made use of.

The building has two rooms, each 13 feet square, the outer of which serves as consulting room, the inner as operating theatre. There are also two small side rooms under the very wide projections of the roof : one is the dispensary, the other the sterilising room. The floor is of cement. The windows are very large and go right up to the roof. That prevents any accumulation of hot air at the top of the room, and every one is astonished to find how cool it is, although corrugated iron buildings are always condemned in the tropics as being intolerably hot. There is no glass in the windows, only fine wire netting to keep out mosquitoes, but there are wooden shutters outside, which are necessary on account of the storms. Along the walls run wide shelves, many of them of the rarest woods. We had no common boards left, and it would have cost much more to have had new ones sawn than to use even the most expensive that we had ready, besides throwing the work weeks backward. Under the roof white calico is stretched tightly as a protection against mosquitoes, which otherwise would find their way in through holes.

During December the waiting-room was got ready and a shed for housing the patients. Both buildings are constructed like large native huts out of unhewn logs and raffia leaves, and I myself, under Mr. Christol's direction, took part in the work. The patients' dormitory measures 42 feet by 19 feet 6 inches. Joseph has a large hut to himself. These buildings lie along both sides of a path about 30 yards long which leads from the iron building to a bay in the river, in which the canoes of the patients are moored. The bay is over-shadowed by a magnificent mango tree.

When the roof of the dormitory was ready, I marked on the floor of beaten earth with a pointed stick sixteen large rectangles, each indicating a bed, with passages left between them. Then the patients and their attendants, who hitherto had been lodged, so far as possible, in a boathouse, were called in. Each patient was put into a rectangle, which was to be his sleeping place, and their attendants were given axes with which to build the bedsteads ; a piece of bast on a peg showed the height they were to have. A quarter of an hour later canoes were going up and down stream to fetch the wood needed, and the beds were ready before nightfall. They consist of four short posts ending in forks, on which tie two strong side-poles, with shorter pieces lying across, the whole bound firmly together with creeper stalks. Dried grass serves as a mattress.

The beds are about 20 inches from the ground, so that boxes, cooking utensils, and bananas can be stored below, and they are broad enough for two or three persons to occupy them at once ; if they do not provide room enough, the attendants sleep on the floor. They bring their own mosquito nets with them.

There is no separation of the sexes in the big shed ;
they arrange themselves in their usual way.   The only
thing I insist on is that the healthy shall not take
possession of a bed while a patient has to sleep on the
ground.   I must soon build some more huts for their
accommodation, as the one dormitory is not enough.
I must also have some rooms in which to isolate
infectious cases, especially the dysentery ones.   The
patients with sleeping sickness, again, I cannot keep
for any length of time in hospital, as they endanger the
health of the whole station, and later on I shall build
a hut for them in a quiet spot on the other side of the
river.   There is plenty of work to do beside the mere
medical treatment.

*

*   *

With the hospital building finished, the doctor's
wife can develop her activity to the full.   In the fowl-
house there was only room for Joseph and myself.
She shares with me the work of teaching Joseph how
to clean and handle the instruments and to prepare
for operations. She also superintends the washing, and it
takes a great deal of trouble to ensure that the dirty and
infected bandages are properly cleaned and sufficiently
boiled.   She appears punctually at ten o'clock, and
stays till twelve, insisting on everything being kept in
good order.

To understand what it means when my wife leaves
her household work to give most of the morning to the
medical work as well as not a few afternoons to the
operations, for which she administers the anæsthetics,
one must know how complicated the simplest style
of housekeeping is in Africa.   This is the result of two

causes : first, the strict division of duties among the native servants, and, second, their unreliability. We have to keep, as is customary, three servants : a boy, a cook, and a washerman. To assign the work of the last-named to either the boy or the cook, as is often done in small households, is impossible in our case, on account of the extra washing which comes to the house from the hospital. Apart from this, a moderately good European maid could do the whole of the work quite well by herself. The cook does nothing but the cooking, the washerman the washing and ironing, and the boy looks after the rooms and the fowls. Each of them, as soon as he has finished his own work, goes off to rest ! So we have to do ourselves whatever work there is which does not belong to either of their strictly defined departments. Women servants are not to be had out here. Mrs. Christol has as nursemaid for her eighteen months old baby girl a native boy of fourteen, M'Buru by name.

Then, again, all one's servants, even the best of them, are so unreliable that they must not be exposed to the slightest temptation. This means that they must never be left alone in the house. All the time they are at work there my wife must be there too, and anything that might be attractive to their dishonesty must be kept locked up. Each morning the cook is given exactly what is to be prepared for our meals, so much rice, fat, and potato ; in the kitchen he keeps just a small supply of salt, flour, and spice, and if he forgets anything, my wife will have to go up the hill again to the house from the hospital in order to give it out to him.

That one can never leave them alone in a room,

that one keeps everything locked up and does not ιrust them with more than the exact amount of foodstuffs, is not taken by the black servants as an insult. They themselves expect us to observe these precautionary measures strictly, in order that they may not be held responsible for any occasional theft. Joseph insists on my locking the dispensary if I go into the dormitory from the iron building for even two minutes, and leave him alone in the consulting-room, from which one goes into the dispensary. If a European does not observe these precautions then his blacks steal his things with a good conscience. What is not locked up " goes for a walk," to use Joseph's language ; you may steal anything from a person who is so careless !

Worse still, however, than this, the negro steals not merely what will be of value to him, but anything that attracts him for the moment. Mr. Rambaud, of Samkita, lost in this way part of a valuable work in several volumes, and there disappeared one day from my bookshelf the piano edition of Wagner's " Meister-singer " and the copy of Bach's Passion Music (S. Matthew), into which I had written the organ accompaniment, which I had worked out very carefully ! This feeling of never being safe from the stupidest piece of theft brings one sometimes almost to despair, and to have to keep everything locked up and turn oneself into a walking bunch of keys adds a terrible burden to life.

*

*   *

If I went simply by what the blacks ask for, I should now have to operate on some one every day ; the people with hernia quarrel as to who shall submit to the knife first ! However, at present we manage to get off with two or three operations a week. For more than this my wife would be unable to manage the necessary preparations and the cleaning and putting away of the instruments afterwards ; nor should I be equal to the work. I have often to operate in the afternoon when I have been busy till one o'clock or even later with bandaging and examination ; and in this land one cannot take so much upon one as in a more temperate climate.

That Joseph can allow himself to collect the vessels with blood in them after an operation and to wash the instruments, is a sign of very high enlightenment. An ordinary negro will touch nothing that is defiled with blood or pus, because it would make him unclean in the religious sense. In many districts of Equatorial Africa it is difficult, or even impossible, to persuade the natives to let themselves be operated on, and why those on the Ogowe even crowd to us for the purpose I do not know. Their readiness is probably connected with the fact that some years ago an army doctor, Jorryguibert by name, stayed some time with the District Commandant at Lambarene, and performed a series of successful operations. He sowed, and I am reaping.

Not long ago I got a rare case of injury to operate on, for which many a famous surgeon might envy me. It was a case of strangulated hernia which protruded under the ribs, the so-called lumbar hernia. There was every imaginable complication present, and when darkness fell I had not finished ; for the final sutures Joseph had to hold the lamp for me. But the patient recovered.

Much notice was attracted by an operation on a boy

who for a year and a half had had a piece of necrosed bone, as long as his hand, projecting from his leg below the knee.   It was a case of osteomyelitis, and the pus secreted stank so horribly that no one could stay near him for long.   The boy himself was reduced to a skeleton, but now he is fat and healthy and is beginning to walk again.

Hitherto all my operations have been successful, and that raises the confidence of the natives to a pitch that almost terrifies me.   What impresses them most of all is the anæsthetics, and they talk a great deal about them. The girls in our school exchange letters with those in a Sunday school at home, and in one of them there was the following piece of news : " Since the Doctor came here we have seen the most wonderful things happen. First of all he kills the sick people ; then he cures them, and after that he wakes them up again."   For anæsthesia seems to the native the same thing as being dead, and similarly if one of them wants to make me understand that he has had an apoplectic fit, he says : " I was dead."

There are sometimes patients who try to show their gratitude.   The man who in August was freed from a strangulated   hernia collected 20 francs among his relations, " in order to pay the Doctor for the expensive thread with which he sewed up my belly."

An uncle of the boy with the sores on his feet, a joiner by trade, put in fourteen days' work for me making cupboards out of old boxes.

A black trader offered me his labourers in order that the roof of my house might be put in order in good time before the rains.

Another came to see me and thank me for having

come out to help the natives, and when he left me he presented me with 20 francs for the medicine chest.

Another patient presented my wife with a kiboko (or sjambok) of hippopotamus hide. It is made in this way: When a hippopotamus is killed, its hide, which is from ½ inch to 1 inch thick, is cut into strips about 1½ inches wide and nearly 5 feet long. One end is nailed to a board, the strip is twisted into a spiral, and the other end is nailed down. When it is dry that supple, sharp - cornered, and justly dreaded instrument of torture is ready.

*

*   *

These last few weeks I have been busy stowing away the supply of drugs, etc., which arrived in October and November. The reserve stock we place in the small iron room on the hill, of which I have had the use since Mr. Ellenberger went away, and which the grateful uncle mentioned above has fitted with the necessary cupboards and shelves. It is true that they do not look handsome, being put together from cases and bearing still the addresses that were painted on them, but we have a place for everything : that is the essential thing. In Africa we learn not to be too exacting.

While I was worrying over the cost of these valuable supplies of medicines, bandages, and lint, the December mail brought me news of fresh gifts which made my heart lighter again. How can we thank sufficiently all our friends and acquaintances ? By the time anything comes to Lambarene it costs about three times its European price, and this increase is accounted for by the cost of packing, which must be very carefully done, of the railway journey, of shipping and unloading, of the voyage, of the colonial import duty, of conveyance up the river, and allowance for the general losses which result from heat or water in the hold or from rough handling at the ports.

Our health continues excellent ; not a trace of fever, though we need a few days' rest.

Just as I close this chapter there arrives at the station an old man with leprosy. He and his wife have come from the Fernando Vaz lagoon, which lies south of Cape Lopez and is connected with Ogowe by one of its smaller mouths. The poor creatures have rowed themselves 250 miles upstream to visit the doctor, and can hardly stand for exhaustion.

THE HOSPITAL AT LAMBARENE.

Showing corrugated iron buildings and huts, with coffee bushes in the foreground.

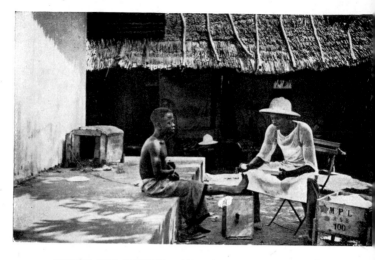

JOSEPH, THE HOSPITAL ASSISTANT, BANDAGING SORES IN
FRONT OF THE HOSPITAL.

NEGRO CHILD WITH ABDOMINAL DROPSY.

CHAPTER V

LAMBARENE, *End of June,* 1914.

AT the end of January and the beginning of February my wife and I were in Talagouga busy looking after Mr. Hermann, a missionary, who was suffering from a bad attack of boils with high fever, and at the same time I treated the sick of the neighbourhood. Among the latter was a small boy who, with every sign of extreme terror, refused to enter the room, and had to be carried in by force. It transpired later that he quite thought the doctor meant to kill and eat him ! The poor little fellow had got his knowledge of cannibalism, not from nursery tales, but from the terrible reality, for even to-day it has not been quite extirpated among the Pahouins. About the area over which it still prevails it is hard to say anything definite, as fear of the heavy penalties attached to it make the natives keep every case as secret as possible. A short time ago, however, a man went from the neighbourhood of Lambarene into some outlying villages to collect arrears of debt, and did not come back. A labourer disappeared in the same way from near Samkita. People who know the country say that " missing " is often to be interpreted as " eaten."

Even the keeping of slaves by natives, though it is no longer acknowledged as such, is not yet a thing of the past, in spite of the war that both Government and missions carry on against it.   I often notice among the attendants of a sick man some whose features are not those of any tribe that is settled here or in the neighbourhood.   But if I ask whether they are slaves, I am assured with a rather peculiar smile that they are only " servants."   The lot of these unacknowledged slaves is by no means a hard one.   They never have to fear ill-treatment, and they never think of escaping and putting themselves under the protection of the Government.   If an inquiry is held, they usually deny obstinately that they are slaves, and it often happens that after a number of years of slavery they are admitted as members of the tribe, thereby becoming free and obtaining a right of domicile in a definite place.   The latter is what they regard as most valuable.

The reason for the continued secret existence of domestic slavery in the district of the lower Ogowe, is to be looked for in the food conditions of the interior. It is the disastrous lot of Equatorial Africa never to have had at any time either fruit-bearing plants or fruit-bearing trees.   The banana stocks, the manioc, the yam, the potato, and the oil palm were introduced from their West Indian islands by the Portuguese, who were the great benefactors of Equatorial Africa.   In the districts where these useful products have not been introduced, or where they are not well established, permanent famine prevails.   Then parents sell their children to districts lower down stream, in order that these, at any rate, may have something to eat.   In the upper course of the N'Gounje, a tributary of the Ogowe, there must be such a famine district ; it is from there that the majority of the domestic slaves on the Ogowe come, and I have patients from there who belong to the "earth eaters." These are driven by hunger to accustom themselves to this practice, and they keep it up even when they have a sufficiency of food.

That the oil palm was imported one can notice evidence to-day, for on the river and round the lakes where there are, or once were, villages, there are whole woods of oil palms, but when one goes about on the main roads into the virgin forest, where there has never been a human settlement, there is not one to be seen.

On our return journey from Talagouga we stayed two days in Samkita with Mr. and Mrs. Morel, the missionaries from Alsace. Samkita is the leopard station, and one of these robbers broke, one night last autumn, into Mrs. Morel's fowl-house. On hearing the cries of their feathered treasures, her husband hurried off to get some one to help, while she kept a look-out in the darkness, for they supposed a native had forced his way in to steal something for his dinner. Then, hearing a noise on the roof, Mrs. Morel went nearer in hopes of identifying the intruder. The latter, however, had already vanished in the darkness with a mighty spring, and when they opened the door twenty-two fowls lay dead on the floor with their breasts torn open. It is only the leopard that kills in this fashion, his chief object being to get blood to drink. His victims were removed, but one of them, stuffed with strychnine, was left lying before the door. Two hours later the leopard returned and devoured it, and while it was writhing in cramp it was shot by Mr. Morel. Shortly before our arrival another leopard had made his appearance in Samkita, and had devoured several goats.

At the house of Mr. Cadier, a missionary, we ate monkey flesh for the first time, for Mr. Cadier is a great sportsman. With me, on the contrary, the blacks are far from pleased, because I use my rifle so little. On one of my journeys we passed a cayman, asleep on a tree which was growing out of the water, and when I merely watched it instead of shooting it the cup of their indignation ran over. " Nothing ever happens with you," the crew exclaimed through their spokesman. " If we were with Mr. Cadier, he would long ago have shot us a couple of monkeys and some birds so that we could have some meat. But you pass close by a cayman and never even touch your shooter ! " I willingly put up with the reproach. Birds which circle above the water I never like shooting ; monkeys are perfectly safe from my weapon. One can often bring down or wound three or four in succession and yet never secure their bodies. They get caught among the thick branches or fall into the undergrowth which covers an impenetrable swamp ; and if one finds the body, one often finds also a poor little baby monkey, which clings, with lamentations, to its dying mother. My chief reason for keeping a gun is to be able to shoot snakes, which swarm on the grass around my house, and the birds of prey which plunder the nests of the weaver bird in the palm trees in front of it.

On our return journey we met a herd of fifteen hippos, who soon plunged into the water on our approach, but a quite young one remained amusing itself on the sandbank, and would not obey its mother when she called to it.

During our absence Joseph had carried out his duties very well, and had treated the surgical cases with intelligence. On his own initiative he had dressed the festering stump of a man's arm with a solution of hydrogen peroxide, which he had to make from biborate of sodium !

The young man who had been mauled by the hippo I found in a very bad state. My three weeks' absence had prevented me from operating at the right time, and he died during the amputation of his leg, which I now hastily undertook. As he drew his last breaths his brother began to look angrily at the companion who had gone with him on the fatal expedition, and had come to the station to help to look after him. He spoke to him also in a low voice, and as the body became cold there began an excited duel of words between them. Joseph drew me aside and explained what it meant. N'Kendju, the companion, had been with the dead man on the expedition, and they had, in fact, gone on his invitation. He was, therefore, according to native law, responsible for him, and could be called to account. That was why he had had to leave his village to stay all these weeks by his friend's bedside, and now that they were taking the dead man back to his village he was expected to go with them, that the case against him might be settled at once. He did not want to go, however, as he knew that it would mean death. I told the brother that I regarded N'Kendju as being now in my service, and that I would not let him go, which led to an angry altercation between him and myself while the body was being placed in the canoe, where the mother and the aunts began the funeral lamentations. He asserted

F

that N'Kendju would not be put to death, but would
only have to pay a fine.   Joseph, however, assured me
that no reliance could be placed on such statements,
and I felt obliged to remain at the river side till they
started, as they would otherwise, no doubt, have
dragged N'Kendju into the canoe by force.

My wife was troubled that while the patient was
breathing his last his brother showed no sign of grief,
and was thinking only of the putting into force of the
legal rights, and she expressed herself angrily about
his want of feeling.   But in that she was no doubt
wronging him.   He was only fulfilling a sacred duty
in beginning at once to take care that the person who,
from his point of view, was responsible for his brother's
death, did not escape the penalty due to him.   For to
a negro it is unthinkable that any such act should
remain unatoned for, a point of view which is thoroughly
Hegelian !   For him the legal side of an event is always
the important one, and a large part of his time is spent
in discussing legal cases.*   The most hardened litigant
in Europe is but a child compared to the negro, and
yet it is not the mere love of litigation that is the latter's
motive ; it is an unspoilt sense of justice, such as is,
on the whole, no longer felt by Europeans.   I was
getting ready one day to tap an old Pahouin who was

* "No other race on a similar level of culture has developed as
strict methods of legal procedure as has the negro.   Many of his
legal forms remind us strongly of those of mediæval Europe."
(*Prof. Boas in " The Ethnical Record," March*, 1904, *p.* 107.)

"Everywhere in Africa where the life of the people has not been
disturbed by outside influences, the people are governed by law.
There is law relating to property, to morality, to the protection of life,
in fact, in many portions of Africa law is more strictly regarded than
in many civilised countries."   (*Booker Washington : " The Story
of the Negro," Vol. I., p.* 70.)

suffering badly from abdominal dropsy, when he said
to me : " Doctor, see that all the water runs off as
soon as possible, so that I can breathe and get about
again. My wife has deserted me because my body
has got so big, and I must go and press for the return
of the money I paid for her at the wedding." On
another occasion a child was brought to me in a most
miserable condition ; its right leg had an open sore
along it right up to the hip. " Why didn't you come
before ? " " Doctor, we couldn't ; there was a palaver
to finish." A palaver means any sort of quarrel
which is brought up for a legal settlement, and the
little ones are discussed in the same detail and with the
same earnestness as the big ones. A dispute involving
a single fowl will keep the village elders employed for a
whole afternoon. Every negro is a law expert.

The legal side of life is extremely complicated with
them, because the limits of responsibility are, according
to our notions, very wide indeed. For a negro's debts
the whole of his family, down to the remotest degree
of relationship, is responsible. Similarly the penalties
are extraordinarily severe. If a man has used another's
canoe illegally for a single day, he must pay the third
of its value as a fine.

Together with this unspoilt sense of justice goes
the fact that the native accepts the punishment as
something obvious and needing no defence, even when
it is, according to our notions, much too severe. If he
did not get punished for an offence, his only conclusion
would be that his victims were remarkably foolish.
Yet the lightest sentence, if unjust, rouses him to great
indignation ; he never forgives it, and he recognises
the penalty as just only if he is really convicted and

obliged to confess. So long as he can lie with the slightest plausibility, he inveighs against his condemnation with most honourable-seeming indignation, even if he is actually guilty. This is a feature in primitive man which every one who has to do with him must take into account.

That N'Kendju ought to pay some compensation to the family of his companion on the unfortunate fishing expedition is obvious, even though he was only so very indirectly responsible for the other's death. But they must get the case against him settled in orderly fashion in the District Court at Lambarene.

*

* *

I am always able to rely on Joseph. True, he can neither read nor write, but in spite of that he never makes a mistake when he has to get a medicine down from the shelf. He remembers the look of the words on the label, and reads this, without knowing the individual letters. His memory is magnificent, and his capacity for languages remarkable. He knows well eight negro dialects, and speaks fairly well both French and English. He is at present a single man, as his wife left him, when he was a cook down on the coast, to go and live with a white man. The purchase price of a new life companion would be about 600 francs (£24), but the money can be paid in instalments. Joseph, however, has no mind to take another wife under these conditions, for he thinks they are an abomination. " If one of us," he said to me, " has not completely paid for his wife, his life is most uncomfortable. His wife does not obey him, and whenever an opportunity offers she taunts him with having no right

PAHOUIN BOYS FROM LAMBARENE.

STUMP OF A MAHOGANY TREE.

to say anything to her, because she has not yet been paid for."

As Joseph does not understand how to save any better than the other natives, I have bestowed on him a money-box in which to save up for the purchase of a wife. Into this goes all his extra pay for sitting up at night or other special services, and all the tips he gets from white patients. How extravagant the " first assistant of the doctor in Lambarene " (as he calls himself) can be, I experienced about this time. He was with me at a store, and while I was buying some nails and screws his eye was caught by a pair of patent leather shoes which, from standing a long time in a. Paris shop window, had got sun-dried and rotten, and had then, like many other odds and ends, found their way to Africa. Although they cost nearly as much as the amount of his monthly wages, he meant to buy them, and warning looks from me were useless, as were also a couple of digs in the ribs which I gave him quietly while we were standing at the counter among a crowd of staring negroes. I could not venture openly to dissuade him, as it would have offended the dealer, who was thankful to get rid of the shoes. So at last I pinched him unperceived as hard as I could just above the back of his thigh till he could stand the pain no longer, and the transaction was broken off. In the canoe I gave him a long lecture on his childish taste for extravagance, with the result that the very next day he went to the store again on the quiet and bought the shoes ! Quite half of what he earns from me he spends in clothes, shoes, ties, and sugar. He dresses much more elegantly than I do.

All through the last few months the work has been

steadily growing. Our hospital is splendidly situated. Upstream and downstream, from places hundreds of kilometres away on the Ogowe and its tributaries, sick people are brought here, and the fact that those who bring them can be lodged here is a further encouragement to come in great numbers. And there is yet another attraction : the fact that I am always at home, unless—and this has happened only two or three times so far—I have to go to some other mission station to treat a missionary who is ill, or some member of his family. Thus the native who has undertaken the trouble and the expense of the journey here from a distance, is sure of seeing me. That is the great advantage which the independent doctor has over one appointed by the Government. The latter is ordered now here, now there, by the authorities, or has to spend a long time with a military column on the march. " And that you have not got to waste so much time on correspondence, reports, and statistics, as we have to, is also an advantage, the reality of which you have not yet grasped," said an army doctor not long ago, during a short chat with me on his way past.

*

*   *

The hut for the sleeping sickness victims is now in course of erection on the opposite bank, and costs me much money and time. When I am not myself superintending the labourers whom we have secured for grubbing up the vegetation and building the hut, nothing is done. For whole afternoons I have to neglect the sick to play the part of foreman there.

Sleeping sickness prevails more widely here than I suspected at first. The chief focus of infection is in the

N'Gounje district, the N'Gounje being a tributary of
the Ogowe about ninety miles from here, but there
are isolated centres round Lambarene and on the lakes
behind N'Gômô.

What is the sleeping sickness ?   How is it spread ?
It seems to have existed in Equatorial Africa from time
immemorial, but it was confined to particular centres,
since there was little or no travelling.   The native
method of trade with the sea coast was for each tribe
to convey the goods to the boundary of its territory,
and there to hand them over to the traders of the
adjoining one.   From my window I can see the place
where the N'Gounje enters the Ogowe, and so far only
might the Galoas living round Lambarene travel.
Any one who went beyond this point, further into the
interior, was eaten.

When the Europeans came, the natives who served
them as boats' crews, or as carriers in their caravans,
moved with them from one district to another, and if
any of them had the sleeping sickness they took it
to fresh places.   In the early days it was unknown on
the Ogowe, and it was introduced about thirty years
ago by carriers from Loango.   Whenever it gets into
a new district it is terribly destructive, and may carry
off a third of the population.   In Uganda, for example,
it reduced the number of inhabitants in six years from
300,000 to 100,000.   An officer told me that he once
visited a village on the Upper Ogowe which had two
thousand inhabitants.   On passing it again two years
later he could only count five hundred ; the rest had
died meanwhile of sleeping sickness.   After some time
the disease loses its virulence, for reasons that we
cannot as yet explain, though it continues to carry off

a regular, if small, number of victims, and then it may begin to rage again as destructively as before.

The first symptom consists of irregular attacks of fever, sometimes light, sometimes severe, and these may come and go for months without the sufferer feeling himself really ill. There are victims who enter the sleep stage straight from this condition of apparent health, but usually severe headaches come during the fever stage. Many a patient have I had come to me crying out : "Oh, doctor ! my head, my head ! I can't stand it any longer ; let me die ! " Again, the sleep stage is sometimes preceded by torturing sleeplessness, and there are patients who at this stage get mentally deranged ; some become melancholy, others delirious. One of my first patients was a young man who was brought because he wanted to commit suicide.

As a rule, rheumatism sets in with the fever. A white man came to me once from the N'Gômô lake district suffering from sciatica. On careful examination, I saw it was the beginning of the sleeping sickness, and I sent him at once to the Pasteur Institute at Paris, where French sufferers are treated. Often, again, an annoying loss of memory is experienced, and this is not infrequently the first symptom which is noticed by those around them. Sooner or later, however, though it may be two or three years after the first attacks of fever, the sleep sets in. At first it is only an urgent need of sleep ; the sufferer falls asleep whenever he sits down and is quiet, or just after meals.

A short time ago a white non-commissioned officer from Mouila, which is six days' journey from here, visited me because, while cleaning his revolver, he had put a bullet through his hand. He stayed at the Catholic mission station, and his black boy accompanied him whenever he came to have his hand dressed, and waited outside. When the N.C.O. was ready to go, there was almost always much shouting and searching for his attendant, till at last, with sleepy looks, the latter emerged from some corner. His master complained that he had already lost him several times because, wherever he happened to be, he was always taking a long nap. I examined his blood and discovered that he had the sleeping sickness.

Towards the finish the sleep becomes sounder and passes at last into coma. Then the sick man lies without either feeling or perception ; his natural motions take place without his being conscious of them, and he gets continually thinner. Meanwhile his back and sides get covered with bed-sores ; his knees are gradually drawn up to his neck, and he is altogether a horrible sight. Release by death has, however, often to be awaited for a long time, and sometimes there is even a lengthy spell of improved health. Last December I was treating a case which had reached this final stage, and at the end of four weeks the relatives hurried home with him that, at least, he might die in his own village. I myself expected the end to come almost at once, but a few days ago I got the news that he had recovered so far as to eat and speak and sit up, and had only died in April. The immediate cause of death is usually pneumonia.

Knowledge of the real nature of sleeping sickness is one of the latest victories of medicine, and is connected with the names of Ford, Castellani, Bruce, Dutton, Koch, Martin, and Leboeuf. The first description of it was given in 1803 from cases observed among the natives of Sierra Leone, and it was afterwards studied also in negroes who had been taken from Africa to the Antilles and to Martinique. It was only in the 'sixties that extensive observations were begun in Africa itself, and these first led to a closer description of the last phase of the disease, no one even suspecting a preceding stage or that there was any connection between the disease and the long period of feverishness. This was only made possible by the discovery that both these forms of sickness had the same producing cause.

Then in 1901 the English doctors, Ford and Dutton, found, on examining with the microscope the blood of fever patients in Gambia, not the malaria parasites they expected, but small, active creatures which on account of their form they compared to gimlets, and named Trypanosomata, *i.e.*, boring-bodies. Two years later the leaders of the English expedition for the investigation of sleeping sickness in the Uganda district found in the blood of a whole series of patients similar little active creatures. Being acquainted with what Ford and Dutton had published on the subject, they asked whether these were not identical with those found in the fever patients from the Gambia region, and at the same time, on examination of their own fever patients, they found the fever to be due to the same cause as produced the sleeping sickness. Thus it was proved that the " Gambia fever " was only an early stage of sleeping sickness.

The sleeping sickness is most commonly conveyed by the *Glossina palpalis*, a species of tsetse fly which flies only by day. If this fly has once bitten any one with sleeping sickness, it can carry the disease to others for a

long time, perhaps for the rest of its life, for the trypanosomes which entered it in the blood it sucked live and
increase and pass in its saliva into the blood of any one
it bites.

Still closer study of sleeping sickness revealed the fact
that it can be also conveyed by mosquitoes, if these
insects take their fill of blood from a healthy person
immediately after they have bitten any one with sleeping
sickness, as they will then have trypanosomes in their
saliva. Thus the mosquito army continues by night
the work which the *glossina* is carrying on all day.
Poor Africa ! *

In its essential nature sleeping sickness is a chronic
inflammation of the meninges and the brain, one, however, which always ends in death, and this ensues because the trypanosomes pass from the blood into the
cerebro-spinal fluid. To fight the disease successfully
it is necessary to kill them before they have passed from
the blood, since it is only in the blood that atoxyl,† one
weapon that we at present possess, produces effects
which can to any extent be relied on ; in the cerebro-
spinal marrow the trypanosomes are comparatively safe
from it. A doctor must, therefore, learn to recognise
the disease in the early stage, when it first produces
fever. If he can do that, there is a prospect of recovery.

In a district, therefore, where sleeping sickness has to
be treated, its diagnosis is a terribly complicated business because the significance of every attack of fever, of

* I must, however, in justice add that the mosquito does not
harbour the trypanosomes permanently, and that its saliva is
poisonous only for a short time after it has been polluted by the
blood of a sleeping sickness victim.
† Atoxyl (meta-arsenic anilid) is a compound of arsenic with an
aniline product.

every persistent headache, of every prolonged attack
of sleeplessness, and of all rheumatic pains must be
gauged with the help of the microscope. Moreover,
this examination of the blood is, unfortunately, by no
means simple, but takes a great deal of time, for it is
only very seldom that these pale, thin parasites, about
one eighteen-thousandth ($\frac{1}{18000}$) of a millimetre long,
are to be found in any considerable number in the
blood. So far I have only examined one case in which
three or four were to be seen together. Even when the
disease is certainly present one can, as a rule, examine
several drops of blood one after another before dis-
covering a single trypanosome, and to scrutinise each
drop properly needs at least ten minutes. I may,
therefore, spend an hour over the blood of a suspected
victim, examining four or five drops without finding
anything, and even then have no right to say there is
no disease ; there is still a long and tedious testing process which must be applied. This consists in taking
ten cubic centimetres of blood from a vein in one of the
sufferer's arms, and keeping it revolving centrifugally
for an hour according to certain prescribed rules, at the
same time pouring off at intervals the outer rings of
blood. The trypanosomes are expected to have
collected into the last few drops, and these are put
under the microscope ; but even if there is again a nega-
tive result, it is not safe to say that the disease is not
present. If there are no trypanosomes to-day, I may
find them ten days hence, and if I have discovered some
to-day, there may be none in three days' time and for a
considerable period after that. A white official, whose
blood I had proved to contain trypanosomes, was
subsequently kept under observation for weeks, in

Libreville, without any being discovered, and it was only in the Sleeping Sickness Institute at Brazzaville that they were a second time proved to be there.

If, then, I wish to treat such patients conscientiously, a couple of them together can tie me for a whole morning to the microscope, while outside there are sitting a score of sick people who want to be seen before dinnertime ! There are also surgical patients whose dressings must be renewed ; water must be distilled, and medicines prepared ; sores must be cleansed, and there are teeth to be drawn ! With this continual drive, and the impatience of the waiting sick, I often get so worried and nervous that I hardly know where I am or what I am doing.

Atoxyl is a frightfully dangerous drug. If the solution is left for some time in the light it decomposes, just like salvarsan, and works as a poison, but even if it is prepared faultlessly and is in perfect condition, it may cause blindness by injuring the nerves of sight. Nor does this depend on the size of the dose ; small ones are often more dangerous than large ones, and they are never of any use. If one begins with too small a dose, in order to see whether the patient can take the drug, the trypanosomes get inured to it ; they become " atoxyl-proof," as it is called, and then can defy the strongest doses. Every five days my sleeping sick come to me for an injection, and before I begin I always ask in trepidation whether any of them have noticed that their sight is not as good as usual. Happily, I have so far only one case of blinding to record, and that was a man in whom the disease had already reached a very advanced stage. Sleeping sickness now prevails from the east coast of Africa right to the west, and from the

Niger in the north-west to the Zambesi in the south-east. Shall we now conquer it ? A systematic campaign against it over this wide district would need many doctors and the cost would be enormous. . . . Yet, where death already stalks about as conqueror, the European States provide in most niggardly fashion the means of stopping it, and merely undertake stupid defensive measures which only give it a chance of reaping a fresh harvest in Europe itself.

*

*   *

After the sleeping sickness it is the treatment of sores and ulcers which takes up most time. They are far more common here than in Europe—one in four of the children in our school has a permanent sore. What is the cause ?

Many sores are caused by sandfleas (*Rynchoprion penetrans*), a species much smaller than the common flea. The female bores into the tenderest part of the toe, preferably under the nail, and grows under the skin to the size of a small lentil. The removal of the insect causes a small wound, and if this gets infected through dirt, there sets in a kind of gangrene, which causes the loss of a joint, or even of a whole toe. Negroes with ten complete toes are almost rarer than those who have one or more mutilated.

It is an interesting fact that the sandflea, which is now a regular plague to Central Africa, is not indigenous there, but was brought over from South America as late as 1872. In ten years from that time it had spread all over the Dark Continent from the Atlantic to the Pacific. In East Africa it is known as the " Jigger." One of the worst species of ants which we have here, the

sangunagenta, is also an importation, having come over
in cases of goods brought from South America.

Besides the sores caused by the sandflea we have the
so-called crawcraw. These generally occur several
together, most commonly on the foot and leg, and are
frightfully painful, but the cause of them we do not yet
know. The treatment consists in cleaning out the sore
with a plug of cotton-wool till it bleeds naturally, when
it is washed out with mercuric chloride and filled with
boracic powder. It is then bandaged and left to itself
for ten days.

Another kind of sore is that of the so-called raspberry
disease (*frambœsia*), which may attack any part of the
body. The name was given because it shows itself first
in largish pustules, covered with a yellow crust, the
removal of which reveals a slightly bleeding surface
which looks exactly like a raspberry stuck on the skin.
There was brought to me once an infant which had got
infected through contact with its mother's breast, and
looked exactly as if it had been first painted over with
some viscous substance and then stuck all over with
raspberries. These pustules may disappear, but for
years afterwards surface sores occur in the most varied
parts of the body.

This disease, which is common in all tropical countries,
is very infectious, and almost all the negroes here have
it at some time or other. The old treatment consisted
in dabbing the sore with a solution of sulphate of copper
(*cupri sulphas*) and giving the patient every day two
grammes of iodide of potassium (*potassii iodidum*) in
water. It has recently been proved that arseno-benzol
injected into the veins of the arm effects a speedy and
permanent cure ; the sores disappear as if by magic.

The worst sores of all are the tropical eating sores (*ulcus phagedenicum tropicum*), which spread in all directions. Not infrequently the whole leg surface is one single sore, in which the sinews and bones show like white islands. The pain is frightful, and the smell is such that no one can stay near the patient for any length of time. The sufferers are placed in a hut by themselves, and have their food brought to them ; there they gradually waste away and die after terrible sufferings. This most horrible of all the different sores is very common on the Ogowe, and merely to disinfect and bandage does no good. The sufferer must be put under an anæsthetic and the sore carefully scraped right down to the sound tissue, during which operation blood flows in streams. The sore is then bathed with a solution of permanganate of potash, but a careful inspection must be made every day so as to detect any new purulent centre that may show itself, as this must at once be scraped out like the others. It is weeks, perhaps months, before the sore is healed, and it will use up half a case of bandages. What a sum it costs us, too, to feed the patient for so long ! But what joy when—limping, indeed, for the healed wounds leave the foot permanently deformed, but rejoicing at his freedom from the old pain and stench—he steps into the canoe for the journey home !

*

*   *

The lepers are another class of sick people who give one much trouble. This disease is caused by a bacillus which is closely allied to that of tuberculosis, and this was discovered in 1871 by a Norwegian doctor, Hansen by name. Isolation, which is always insisted on where possible, is not to be thought of here, and I often have four or five lepers among the other sick folk in the hospital. The most remarkable fact about it is that we have to assume that the infection passes from one individual to another, although no one has yet discovered how it does so, or succeeded in producing infection experimentally. The only drug we have at our disposal for fighting this disease is the so-called Chaulmoogra oil (*oleum gynocardiæ*), which is obtained from the seed of a tree in Further India. It is expensive, and usually comes into the market adulterated. I obtain what I want through a retired missionary, Mr. Delord, a native of French Switzerland, who had a great deal to do with leprosy when he worked in New Caledonia, and can get supplies direct from a reliable source. Following a hint from him I administer the nauseous drug in a mixture of sesame and earth-nut oils (*huile d'arachides*), which makes it more tolerable for taking. Recently the administration of Chaulmoogra oil by subcutaneous injection has also been recommended.

A real cure of leprosy is beyond our powers, but a great improvement in a patient's health can be effected, and the disease can be reduced to a state of quiescence which lasts so long that it is practically equivalent to a cure. The attempts which have been made in recent years to cure the disease by means of a serum prepared from the bacillus that causes it, and known under the name of Nastin, allow us to hope that some day we shall be able to fight it effectively in this way.

With swamp fever, or tropical malaria, I have, unfortunately, like every other doctor in the tropics, plenty to do. To the natives it is merely natural that

every one of them should from time to time have fever
with shivering fits, but children are the worst sufferers.
As a result of this fever the spleen, as is well known,
swells and becomes hard and painful, but with them it
sometimes projects into the body like a hard stone from
under the left ribs, not seldom reaching as far as the navel.
If I place one of these children on the table to examine
him, he instinctively covers the region of the spleen
with his arms and hands for fear I should inadvertently
touch the painful stone.   The negro who has malaria
is a poor, broken-down creature who is always tired and
constantly plagued with headache, and finds even light
work a heavy task. Chronic malaria is known to be
always accompanied by anæmia. The drugs available
for its treatment are arsenic and quinine, and our cook,
our washerman, and our boy each take 7 to 8 grains
(half a gram) of the latter twice a week.   There is
a preparation of arsenic called " Arrhenal," which
enormously enhances the effect of the quinine, and I give
it freely to white and black alike in subcutaneous
injections.

Among the plagues of Africa tropical dysentery must
not be forgotten. This disease, also, is caused by a
special kind of amœba, which settles in the large
intestine and injures the membrane. The pain is
dreadful, and day and night alike, without inter-
mission, the sufferer is constantly wanting to empty the
bowels, and yet passes nothing but blood. Formerly
the treatment of this dysentery, which is very common
here, was a tedious process and not really very successful. The drug used was powdered ipecacuanha root,
but it could seldom be administered in sufficient
quantities to act effectively, because when taken

through the mouth it caused vomiting. For some years, however, use has been made of a preparation of the essential principle contained in this root, under the title of emetin (*emetinum hydrochloricum*). Six to eight cubic centimetres of a 1 per cent. solution of this is injected subcutaneously for several days in succession, and this is followed at once by a great improvement and usually by a permanent cure ; in fact, the results attained border on the miraculous. There is no need for care about diet ; the patient can eat what he likes— hippopotamus steak, if he is black ; potato salad, if he is white. If a doctor could effect no cures in the tropics beyond what these newly-discovered means of healing, arseno-benzol and emetin, make possible, it would still be worth his while to come out here. At the fact that a great part of the labour entailed upon a doctor in the tropics consists in combating various diseases, each one more loathsome than the last, which have been brought to these children of nature by Europeans, I can here only hint. But what an amount of misery is hidden behind the hint !

*

*　　　　*

As to operations, one undertakes, naturally, in the forest only such as are urgent and which promise a successful result. The one I have had to perform oftenest is that for hernia, a thing which afflicts the negroes of Central Africa much more than it does white people, though why this should be so we do not know. They also suffer much oftener than white people from strangulated hernia, in which the intestine becomes constricted and blocked, so that it can no longer empty itself. It then becomes enormously inflated by the gases which form, and this causes terrible pain. Then after several days of torture death takes place, unless the intestine can be got back through the rupture into the abdomen. Our ancestors were well acquainted with this terrible method of dying, but we no longer see it in Europe because every case is operated upon as soon as ever it is recognised. " Let not the sun go down upon your—strangulated hernia," is the maxim continually impressed upon medical students. But in Africa this terrible death is quite common. There are few negroes who have not as boys seen some man rolling in the sand of his hut and howling with agony till death came to release him. So now, the moment a man feels that his rupture is a strangulated one— rupture is far rarer among women—he begs his friends to put him in a canoe and bring him to me.

How can I describe my feelings when a poor fellow is brought me in this condition ? I am the only person within hundreds of miles who can help him. Because I am here and am supplied by my friends with the necessary means, he can be saved, like those who came before him in the same condition and those who will come after him, while otherwise he would have fallen a victim to the torture. This does not mean merely that I can save his life. We must all die. But that I can save him from days of torture, that is what I feel as my great and ever new privilege. Pain is a more terrible lord of mankind than even death himself.

So, when the poor, moaning creature comes, I lay my hand on his forehead and say to him : " Don't be afraid ! In an hour's time you shall be put to sleep, and when you wake you won't feel any more pain." Very soon he is given an injection of omnipon ; the doctor's wife is called to the hospital, and, with Joseph's help, makes everything ready for the operation. When that is to begin she administers the anæsthetic, and Joseph, in a long pair of rubber gloves, acts as assistant.

The operation is finished, and in the hardly lighted dormitory I watch for the sick man's awaking. Scarcely has he recovered consciousness when he stares about him and ejaculates again and again : " I've no more pain ! I've no more pain ! " . . . His hand feels for mine and will not let it go. Then I begin to tell him and the others who are in the room that it is the Lord Jesus who has told the doctor and his wife to come to the Ogowe, and that white people in Europe give them the money to live here and cure the sick negroes. Then I have to answer questions as to who these white people are, where they live, and how they know that the natives suffer so much from sickness. The African sun is shining through the coffee bushes into the dark shed, but we, black and white, sit side by side and feel that we know by experience the meaning of the words : " And all ye are brethren " (Matt. xxiii. 8). Would that my generous friends in Europe could come out here and live through one such hour !

CHAPTER VI

LUMBERMEN AND RAFTSMEN IN THE PRIMEVAL FOREST

CAPE LOPEZ, *July 25th–29th*, 1914

AN abscess, for the opening of which the help of the military doctor at Cape Lopez seemed to be necessary, compelled me about this time to go down to the coast, but we had scarcely got there when it fortunately burst, and the risk of further complications was avoided. My wife and I were kindly entertained at the house of a factory employee called Fourier, whose wife had spent two months that summer at Lambarene, awaiting her confinement at our house. Monsieur Fourier is a grandson of the French philosopher Fourier (1772—1837), in whose social theories I was much interested when a student in Paris. Now one of his great-grandchildren has entered the world under our roof !

I cannot yet move about, so spend the whole day in an armchair on the verandah with my wife, looking out over the sea and inhaling with enjoyment the fresh sea breezes. That there is a breeze at all is a delight to us, for in Lambarene there is never any wind except during the short storms, which are known as tornadoes. This time of leisure I will employ in writing something about the life of the lumbermen and the raftsmen on the Ogowe.

It was only about thirty years ago that attempts were first made to exploit the great forests of West and Equatorial Africa, but the work is not as easy as might be thought. Magnificent timber is there in any quantity, but how fell and transport it ? At present the only timber on the Ogowe that has any commercial value is that which is near the river. The most magnificent tree a kilometre from the water is safe from the axe, for what is the good of felling it if it cannot be taken away ?

Why not build light railways, then, to convey the logs to the water ? That question will be asked only by those who do not know what a forest in Equatorial Africa is like. The ground on which it stands is nothing but a mass of gigantic roots and swamp. To prepare the ground for even 200 or 300 yards of light railway means cutting down the trees, getting rid of their roots, and filling up the swamp ; and that would cost more than a hundred tons of the finest timber would fetch at Cape Lopez. It is, therefore, only at the most favourable spots that light railways can be built cheaply enough. In these forests one learns how impotent man is when pitted against Nature !

Work, then, has, as a rule, to be carried on in a primitive way, and this for the further reason, also, that only primitive men can be got for labourers, and not a sufficient number even of them. The introduction of Annamites and Chinese has been talked of, but it is a hopeless proposal. Foreigners are of no use in the African forest, because they cannot endure the heat and the camp life in it, and, moreover, cannot live on the foods produced locally.

The first thing to be done is to choose the right place

for work. In the virgin forest the trees grow in the
most capricious fashion, and it pays to fell them only
where there is near the water's edge a considerable
number of the kind of trees required. These places are
generally some distance within the forest, but when
the river is high, are usually connected with the latter
by some narrow watercourse, or by a pond, which at
such times becomes a lake. The natives know well
enough where these places are, but they keep the
knowledge to themselves, and make a point of mislead-
ing any white man who comes into their neighbourhood
to look for them. One European told me that the
natives of a certain village kept taking from him for
two months liberal presents of brandy, tobacco, and
cloth while they went out with him every day on the
search for such a place, but not a single one was
discovered which seemed to promise profitable exploita-
tion. At last, from a conversation which he happened
to overhear, he learnt that they purposely took him
past all the favourable spots, and then their friendly
relations came to a sudden end. Of the timber
that stands near enough to the river to be easily
transported, nearly the whole has already been felled.

About half the forest area has been put, through
concessions, into the hands of big European companies.
The rest is free, and any one, white or black, can fell
timber there as he pleases. But even in the woodlands
covered by the concessions the companies often allow
the natives to fell trees as freely as they can in the other
parts, on the one condition that they sell the timber
to the company itself, and not to other dealers.

The important thing, after all, is not to own woods,
but to have timber for sale, and the timber which the

negroes cut down on their own account and then offer
to the company works out cheaper than what the
latter get through their contract labour.   On the other
hand, the supply from the free natives is so uncertain
that it cannot be relied upon for trade purposes.   They
may take it into their heads to celebrate a festival,
or to have a big fishing expedition just when the demand
for timber is greatest, so the companies, while they buy
all they can from the natives, also keep their own
labourers constantly at work.

＊

＊   ＊

When a suitable spot has been discovered, there come
to it either the men of a village who have agreed to
exploit it together, or the white man with his labourers,
and huts are erected to live in.   The great difficulty is
food.   One is faced with the problem of securing supplies for from sixty to one hundred men for weeks and
months together, and that in the middle of the virgin
forest.   The nearest village and the nearest plantations
are perhaps twenty-five miles away, and only to be
reached by a weary struggle through jungle and swamp.
Unfortunately, too, the staple foods of banana and
manioc * are bulky, and therefore troublesome to
transport ; moreover, they only keep good for a few
days.   The great drawback attaching to Equatorial

* Manioc, better known perhaps to English readers as cassava,
belongs to the Euphorbiaceæ.   The two chief kinds are Manihot
utilissima, the bitter, which contains the hydrocyanic acid, and
Manihot Aipi, the sweet, which is harmless.   The roots are 3 feet
long and 6 to 9 inches in diameter, filled with milky juice.   The
starch as prepared for food is known first as Brazilian arrowroot, and
this, when further prepared, as the tapioca of commerce.   (*Encycl.
Brit.*, *s.v.*)

Africa is that none of its food products keep long. Bananas and manioc ripen the whole year through, now freely, now sparingly, according to the time of year, but bananas go bad six days after gathering, and manioc bread ten days after it is made. The manioc root by itself is unusable, as there are poisonous species which contain cyanic acid, to get rid of which the roots are soaked for some days in running water. Stanley lost three hundred carriers because they too hastily ate manioc root which had not been washed long enough. When it is taken out of the water it is crushed and rubbed, and undergoes fermentation, and this produces a kind of tough, dark dough, which is moulded into thin sticks and wrapped in leaves for preservation. Europeans find this a very poor food.

Since, then, the regular provision of local foodstuffs is so difficult, these native timber workers have to reconcile themselves to living on rice and preserved foods from Europe. This means mostly cheap tins of sardines, prepared specially for export to the inland regions of Africa, and of these the stores always have a big supply in stock. Variety is secured by means of tinned lobster, tinned asparagus, and Californian fruits. The expensive tinned stuff which the well-to-do European denies himself as too expensive, the negro, when felling timber, eats from necessity !

And shooting ? In the real forest shooting is impossible. There is, indeed, wild life in plenty, but how is it to be discovered and pursued in the thick jungle ? Good shooting is only to be had where grassland or treeless marshes alternate with the forest, but in such places there is usually no timber to be felled. Thus, paradox though it seems, it is nowhere easier to starve than amid the luxurious vegetation of the game-haunted forests of Equatorial Africa !

How the timber-workers manage to get through the day with the tsetse fly, and through the night with the mosquito, it is hard to tell. Often, too, they have to work for days together up to the hips in water. Naturally they all suffer from fever and rheumatism.

. The felling of the trees is very troublesome work because of the thickness of the trunks. Moreover, the giants of the forest do not grow up out of the earth round and smooth ; they are anchored to the ground by a row of strong, angular projections, which as they leave the stems become the main roots, and act as buttresses. Mother Nature, as though she had studied under the best architects, gives these forest giants the only sort of protection which could be effective against the force of the tornadoes.

In many cases the hewing of the trees at ground level is not to be thought of. The axe can begin its work only at the height of a man's head, or it may even be necessary to erect a scaffold on which the hewers can then stand.

Several men must toil hard for days before the axe can finish its work, and even then the tree does not always fall. It is tangled into a single mass with its neighbours by powerful creepers, and only when these have been cut through does it come, with them, to the ground. Then begins the process of cutting up. It is sawn, or hewn with axes, into pieces from 12 to 15 feet long, until the point is reached at which the diameter is less than 2 feet. The rest is left, and decays, and with it those portions also which are too thick, that is, which are more than 5 to 5½ feet in diameter, as such huge pieces are too awkward to handle.

The felling and cutting up of the trees takes place as a rule in the dry season, that is, between June and October. The next work is to clear the track by which these mighty logs, weighing sometimes as much as three tons, are to be rolled to the nearest piece of water. Then begins a contest with the roots which have been left in the ground and the huge tree tops which are lying upon it, and not infrequently the mighty trunk itself has in its fall embedded itself three feet in the soil. But in time the track is got fairly ready, the portions which run through swamp being filled up with wood. The pieces—spoken of as "billets" (French, *billes*)—are rolled on to the track, thirty men, with rhythmical shouts, pushing and shoving at each one and turning it slowly over and over on its axis. If a piece is very large, or not quite round, human strength may not suffice, and the movement is effected by means of jacks. Then a hillock in the way may present a difficulty to be overcome ; or, again, the wood-packing in the swamp may give way ! The thirty men in an afternoon's work seldom move one of these "billets" more than eighty to ninety yards.

And time presses ! All the timber must be got to the pond to be ready for the high water at the end of November and the beginning of December, since it is only just then that the pond is in connection with the rivers. Any timber that misses this connection remains in the forest, and is reduced to such a condition by the parasitic wood-insects—especially by a species of Bostrichid beetle—that it is not worth buying. At best it can be saved when the spring high water comes,

RAFT OF OKOUME WOOD AND MAHOGANY BEING FLOATED DOWN THE OGOWE RIVER.

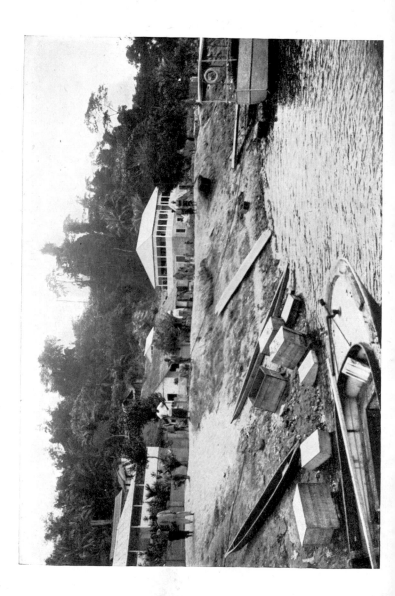

but that is often not high enough to connect all the ponds, and if the timber has to stay there till the next autumn flood it is assuredly lost.

Occasionally, once perhaps in ten years, even the autumn flood does not rise high enough, and then the season's work is wholly lost on many timber-working sites. This happened last autumn (1913), and many middle-sized and small trading firms are reported to have been nearly ruined. The male populations of many villages, too, after labouring for months, did not earn enough to cover their debts for the rice and tinned foods that they had had to buy.

At last the timber is in the river, moored to the jungle on the bank with ropes of creepers, and the white trader comes to buy what the negroes of the different villages have to offer him. And here caution is necessary. Is the timber really of the kind desired, or have the negroes smuggled in among it pieces of some other tree with a similar bark and similar veining which stood at the water's edge ? Is it all freshly cut, or are there some last year's logs, or even some of the year before last, which have had their ends sawn off to make them look new ? The inventive skill of the negroes with a view to cheating in timber borders on the incredible ! Let the newcomer be on his guard ! For example : In Libreville Bay a young English merchant was to buy for his firm some ebony, a heavy wood, which comes into the market in short logs. The Englishman reported with satisfaction that he had secured some huge pieces of magnificent ebony, but no sooner had his first purchase reached England than he received a telegram saying that what he had bought and despatched for ebony was nothing of the kind ; that

his expensive stuff was worthless, and he himself
responsible for the loss involved ! The fact was that
the negroes had sold him some hard wood which they
had allowed to lie for several months in the black
swamp. There it had soaked in the colour so thoroughly
that at the ends and to a certain depth all over it
seemed to be the finest ebony ; the inner part, however,
was of a reddish colour. The inexperienced white man
had neglected to test his bargain by sawing one of the
logs in two !

The dealer, then, measures and purchases the timber.
The measuring is a difficult job, as he has to jump about
on the logs, which turn over in the water with his
weight. Then he pays up half the purchase money,
keeping the rest till the timber, on which the trade
mark of his firm is now cut, has been brought safely
down to the coast. Sometimes, however, it happens
that natives sell the timber four or five times over,
pocketing the money each time and then disappearing
into the forest till the transaction has been forgotten,
or till the white man is tired of spending time and
money in going after the swindlers, by whom, indeed,
he is not likely to be indemnified, seeing that, long
before he finds them, they will have spent the money
in tobacco and other things.

*

*   *

Next comes the building of the rafts, or floats, for
which neither rope nor wire is needed, as the supple
creepers of the forest are cheaper and better than either,
and can be had as thin as a finger or as thick as one's
arm. From 60 to 100 of the 12 to 15 feet trunks are
arranged one behind the other in two rows and bound

together, so that the raft is from 25 to 30 feet broad, and about 130 feet long, and its weight may be as much as 200 tons. Long planks are also bound upon it on a regular plan, and these give it the necessary strength and firmness. Next huts of bamboo and raffia leaves are built upon it, and a special platform of logs is coated with clay to serve as a fireplace for cooking. Powerful steering-oars are fixed in front and behind in strong forks, so that the course of the raft can be to some extent guided, and as each of these needs at least six men to work it, there must be a crew of between fifteen and twenty men. Then when all the bananas and manioc sticks that can be procured have been placed upon it, the voyage begins.

The crew must know well the whereabouts of the continually shifting sandbanks, in order to avoid them, and these, covered as they are with brown water, are very hard to detect at any considerable distance. If the raft strikes one, there is no way of getting it afloat again but by releasing from it one by one the logs which have got fixed in the sand, and putting them back again afterwards. Sometimes the raft has to be taken entirely to pieces and re-made, a proceeding which under those conditions takes a week and involves the loss of a certain number of the logs, which the stream carries away during the work. Time, too, is precious, for provisions are usually not too abundant, and the further they get down the Ogowe, the harder it is to get more. For a few wretched bananas the people of the villages on the lower Ogowe exact from the hungry raftsmen a franc, or a franc and a half; or they may refuse to supply anything at all.

It happens not infrequently during the voyage that

the crew sell some of the good logs in the raft to other negroes, and replace them with less valuable ones of exactly the same sizes, putting the firm's trade mark upon these with deceptive accuracy. These inferior pieces that have been thrown away in the forest have been lying in dozens ever since the last high water, either on the sandbanks or in the little bays on the river banks, and there are said to be villages which keep a big store of them of all possible sizes. The good timber which has been taken from the raft is later made unrecognisable, and is sold over again to a white man.

Other reasons, too, the white man has for anxiety about his raft on its way down. In so many days the ship which is to take the timber will be at Cape Lopez, and the rafts have till then to come in : the crew have been promised a handsome bonus if they arrive in good time. But if the tomtom is sounded in a river-bank village as they pass, they may succumb to the temptation to moor the raft and join in the festivities—for two, four, six days ! Meanwhile the ship waits at Cape Lopez and the trader must pay for the delay a fine which turns his hoped-for profitable stroke of business into a serious loss.

The 200 miles (350 kilometres) from Lambarene to Cape Lopez usually take such a raft fourteen days. The, at first, comparatively quick rate of progress slows down towards the end, for about fifty miles from the river mouth the tide makes itself felt in the river. For this reason, too, the river water can no longer be drunk, and as there are no springs within reach, the canoe which is attached to the raft is filled in good time with fresh water. From now on progress can be made only with the ebb tide and when the flood tide sets in the raft is moored to the bank with a creeper as thick as a man's arm, so that it may not be carried back upstream.

*

*   *

The next step is to get the raft into a narrow, winding side stream about twenty miles long which enters the sea through the southern shore of Cape Lopez Bay. If it is swept into any of the other arms which have their outlet in the middle of the bay it is lost, for the strong current of the rivers, which, after being dammed up by the flood tide, rushes down at five miles an hour, carries it right out to sea. Through the southern arm, however, it comes out into a strip of shallow water which runs along the coast, and over this it can be navigated with long poles to Cape Lopez. Here again, if the raft gets a few yards too far from the shore so that the punting-poles cannot touch bottom, it can no longer be guided and gets swept out to sea, and within these last ten miles a mighty contest often develops between the crew and the elements. If a land breeze gets up there is hardly anything to be done. If, indeed, the position of the raft is noticed at Cape Lopez, they try to send a boat to it with an anchor and a cable, and that may save it if the waves are not so strong as to break it up. But if that happens, there is only one thing for the crew to do, if they do not wish to be lost also, and that is to leave the raft, in the canoe—and at the right moment. For once out at the mouth of the bay, no canoe can make its way back to Cape Lopez in the teeth of the ebb tide and the regular current of the river. The flat, keelless vessels which are used in the river are useless in a contest with the waves.

H

In this way more than one raft has been lost, and more than one crew has disappeared in the waves. One of my white patients once found himself on one of these unlucky rafts. They were driven out to sea after dark by a breeze which got up quite unexpectedly, and the force of the waves made it hopeless to think of escaping in the canoe. The raft was beginning to break up when a motor longboat came to the rescue, some one on the shore having noticed the lantern which the despairing men had waved to and fro as they drove past, and sent the rescue boat, which happened fortunately to have its steam up, in pursuit of the moving light.

Brought safely to Cape Lopez, the raft is taken to pieces and the logs go into " the park." At the most sheltered part of the bay two rows of tree-trunks are bound together so as to form a sort of double chain. This is effected by driving into the trunks iron wedges which end in rings through which strong wire ropes are drawn. This double chain of logs protects the calm water from the movement of the sea, and behind this " breakwater," or boom, float as many logs as there is room for. The logs are further fastened together by other wire ropes, running through iron rings which have been driven into them, and every two or three hours a watchman goes round to see whether the boom is all right, whether the rings are still holding, and whether the continual rubbing in the rings and the frequent bending with the up and down movement of the water has not made the wire ropes worn and unsafe. But often the utmost foresight and care is useless. A rope in the breakwater gives way during the night without any one noticing it, and when in the morning the owner of the logs comes to inspect them, they have journeyed out to sea, never to return. Some months ago an English firm lost in this way, in a single night, timber worth something like £1,600 (40,000 francs). But if a tornado comes there is no controlling anything. The huge trunks in the park plunge about like dolphins bewitched, and finally make an elegant jump over the boom into the free water beyond.

＊

＊   ＊

Thus every day that the raft lies in the bay brings a risk, and anxiously is the ship awaited which is to take the logs away. No sooner has it arrived than the motor boats tow raft after raft to its landward side, those that are to be shipped having been prepared first by having wire ropes run through a line of rings at each end. Negroes jump about on the tossing raft, and knock the two rings out of the log that is to be shipped next, so that it floats free of the raft, and then they slip round it the chain with which it is to be hoisted on board. This needs a tremendous amount of skill, for if a labourer falls into the water from the wet and slippery surface of a rolling log he will probably get his legs crushed between these two or three-ton masses of wood which are continually dashing against one another.

From the verandah I can watch through my glasses some negroes occupied with this work, which is made much harder for them by the delightful breeze I am enjoying, and I know that if a tornado comes, or even a really stiff breeze, the rafts which are lying along the ship's side will certainly be lost.

The losses in timber, then, between the places where it is felled and its successful hoisting on board ship, are tremendous, and the lagoons near the mouth of the Ogowe are veritable timber graveyards. Hundreds and hundreds of gigantic tree trunks stick out of the mud there, the majority being trees which could not be got away at the right time and were left to rot, till a bigger flood than usual carried them out to the river. When they got to the bay, wind and tide carried them into the lagoons, from which they will never emerge. At this present minute I can count, with the help of my glasses, some forty trunks which are tossing about in the bay, to remain the plaything of ebb and flood and wind till they find a grave either in the lagoons or in the ocean.

As soon as the raft has been safely delivered the crew make haste to get back up the river, either in their canoe or in a steamer, in order that they may not starve in Cape Lopez, for all the fresh provisions in the port town have to be brought some 125 miles down the river from the interior, since nothing of the kind can be grown in the sands of the coast or the marshes of the river mouth. When they have got back home, and have been paid off by the purchaser of the timber, quantities of tobacco, brandy, and all sorts of goods are bought by them at the latter's store. As rich men, according to native notions, they return to their villages, but in a few weeks, or even earlier, the whole of the money has run through their fingers, and they look out for a new place at which to begin their hard work over again.

The export of timber from Cape Lopez is increasing steadily ; at the present time (1914) it amounts to about 150,000 tons a year. The chief sorts dealt in are mahogany, which the natives call *ombega*, and okoume

A LITTLE PLANTATION OF BANANAS ON THE MARGIN OF THE UNTOUCHED FOREST.

NATIVE HOUSES AT LAMBARÉNÉ

(*Aucoumea klaineana*), the so-called false mahogany. The latter is softer than real mahogany, and is used mostly for making cigar-boxes, but it is employed also for furniture, and has a great future before it. Many species of it are almost more beautiful than the real mahogany.

If the timber is left too long in the water it is attacked by the boring mollusc, the *teredo navalis* (French *taret*). This is a small worm-like creature, really a kind of mussel, which eats a passage for itself straight to the centre of the log. For this reason any timber that has to wait a long time for the ship is rolled on to the shore, and advantage is usually taken of this to hew off the sap wood, so that the trunk becomes a square beam.

But besides the okoume and mahogany there are many other valuable kinds of wood on the Ogowe. I will mention the *ekewasengo*, or rosewood (*bois de rose*), and coralwood (*bois de corail*), both of which have a beautiful red colour, and the ironwood, which is so hard that in the sawmill at N'Gômô there are cog-wheels in use that are made of it. There grows here also a wood which, when planed, looks like white *moiré* silk.

The finest woods, however, are not exported, because they are not yet known in European markets, and are, therefore, not in demand. When they do become known and sought after, the Ogowe timber trade will become even more important than it is to-day. The reputation of being the best wood expert on the Ogowe belongs to Mr. Haug, one of the missionaries at N'Gômô, who has a valuable collection of specimens of every kind of it. At first I could not understand how it is that everybody here, even people who have nothing to do with the timber trade, is so interested in the different kinds of wood.   In the course of time, however, and thanks to continual intercourse with timber merchants, I have myself become, as my wife says, a timber fanatic.

CHAPTER VII

SOCIAL PROBLEMS IN THE FOREST

WRITTEN WHILE ON THE RIVER, *July 30th—Aug. 2nd*, 1914.

I AM again fit for work, and the skipper of a small steamer, which belongs to a trading firm at N'Djôli, has been kind enough to take us with him to Lambarene, but our progress is only slow, as we have a heavy cargo of kerosene. This comes in square tins, each holding four gallons (eighteen litres), straight from the U.S.A. to the Ogowe, and the natives are beginning to use it freely.

I am profiting by the long voyage to arrange and clear my ideas as to the social problems which, to my astonishment, I have come across in the forest. We talk freely in Europe about colonisation, and the spread of civilisation in the colonies, but without making clear to ourselves what these words mean.

But are there really social problems in the forest ? Yes ; one has only to listen for ten minutes to conversation between any two white men, and one will certainly hear them touch on the most difficult of them all, viz., the labour problem. People imagine in Europe that as many labourers as are wanted can always be found among the savages, and secured for very small wages. The real fact is the very opposite. Labourers are nowhere more difficult to find than

among primitive races, and nowhere are they paid so
well in proportion to the work they do in return. This
comes from their laziness, people say ; but is the negro
really so lazy ? Must we go a little deeper into the
problem ?

Any one who has seen the population of a native
village at work, when they have to clear a piece of virgin
forest in order to make a new plantation, knows that
they are able to work enthusiastically, and with all
their might, for weeks together. This hardest of all
work, I may say in passing, is forced upon every
village triennially. The banana exhausts the soil with
extraordinary rapidity, so that every three years they
must lay out a new plantation, manured by the ashes
of the jungle, which they cut down and burn. For
my part I can no longer talk ingenuously of the
laziness of the negro after seeing fifteen of them spend
some thirty-six hours in almost uninterrupted rowing
in order to bring up the river to me a white man who
was seriously ill.

The negro, then, under certain circumstances works
well, but—only so long as circumstances require it.
The child of nature—here is the answer to the puzzle—
is always a casual worker.

In return for very little work nature supplies the
native with nearly everything that he requires for his
support in his village. The forest gives him wood,
bamboos, raffia leaves, and bast for the building of a
hut to shelter him from sun and rain. He has only to
plant some bananas and manioc, to do a little fishing
and shooting, in order to have by him all that he really
needs, without having to hire himself out as a labourer
and to earn regular wages. If he does take a situation,

it is because he needs money for some particular object ; he wishes to buy a wife, or his wife, or his wives, want some fine dress material, or sugar, or tobacco ; he himself wants a new axe, or hankers after rum or cheap spirits, or would like to wear boots and a suit of khaki.

There are, then, various needs differing in number with the individual, but all lying outside the regular struggle for existence, which bring the child of nature to hire himself out for work. If he has no definite object in view for which to earn money he stays in his village. If he is at work anywhere and finds that he has earned enough to supply his heart's desires, he has no reason for troubling himself any further, and he returns to his village, where he can always find board and lodging.

The negro, then, is not idle, but he is a free man ; hence he is always a casual worker, with whose labour no regular industry can be carried on. This is what the missionary finds to be the case on the mission station and in his own house on a small scale, and the planter or merchant on a large one. When my cook has accumulated money enough to let him gratify the wishes of his wife and his mother-in-law, he goes off without any consideration of whether we still want his services or not. The plantation owner is left in the lurch by his labourers just at the critical time when he must wage war on the insects that damage the cocoa plant. Just when there comes from Europe message after message about timber, the timber merchant cannot find a soul to go and fell it, because the village happens at the moment to be out on a fishing expedition, or is laying out a new banana plot. So we are all filled with righteous indignation at the lazy negroes, though the real reason why we cannot get them is that they have not yet learnt to understand what we really mean by continuous work.

There is, therefore, a serious conflict between the needs of trade and the fact that the child of nature is a free man. The wealth of the country cannot be exploited because the native has so slight an interest in the process. How train him to work ? How compel him ?

" Create in him as many needs as possible ; only so can the utmost possible be got out of him," say the State and commerce alike. The former imposes on him involuntary needs in the shape of taxes. With us every native above fourteen pays a poll tax of five francs a year, and it is proposed to double it. If that is done, a man with two wives and seven children will contribute £4 (100 francs) a year, and have to provide a corresponding amount either of labour or of products of the soil. The trader encourages voluntary needs in him by offering him wares of all sorts, useful ones such as clothing material or tools, unnecessary ones such as tobacco and toilet articles, and harmful ones like alcohol. The useful ones would never be enough to produce an amount of labour worth mentioning. Useless trifles and rum are almost more effective. Just consider what sort of things are offered for sale in the forest ! Not long ago I got the negro who manages for a white man a little shop close to a small lake, miles away from civilisation, to show me all his stock. Behind the counter stood conspicuous the beautiful white painted cask of cheap spirits. Next to it stood the boxes of tobacco leaves and the tins of kerosene. Further on was a collection of knives, axes, saws, nails, screws, sewing machines, flat-irons, string for making fishing-nets, plates, glasses, enamelled dishes of all sizes, lamps, rice, tinned stuff of every variety, salt, sugar, blankets, dress material, muslin for mosquitoes, Gillette safety razors (!), collars and ties in rich variety, blouses and chemises trimmed with lace, corsets, elegant shoes, openwork stockings, gramophones, concertinas, and fancy articles of all sorts. Among the last named was a plate, resting on a stand, of which there were several dozen. " What is that ? " I asked. The negro moved a lever in the bottom part and a little musical box at once began to play. " This is my best paying article," said he. " All the women in the neighbourhood want one of these plates, and plague their husbands till they have earned enough to buy one ! "

It is true that taxes and new needs can make a negro work more than he used to, but they do not train him to work, or only to a small extent. They make him anxious for money and for enjoyment, but not reliable or conscientious. If he does take service anywhere, he only thinks how he can get most money for least work, and he works only so long as his employer is near. Just recently I engaged some day labourers to build a new hut for the hospital, but when I came in the evening to see the work, nothing had been done. On the third or fourth day I got angry, but one of the blacks—and one who was by no means the worst of them—said to me : " Doctor, don't shout at us so ! It is your own fault. Stay here and we shall work, but if you are in the hospital with the sick folk, we are alone and do no-thing." Now I have adopted a plan, and when I engage any day labourers I arrange to have two or three hours free. During this time I make them work till their dark skins glisten with sweat, and so I manage to get a certain amount done.

Increasing their needs does effect something, but not much. The child of nature becomes a steady worker only so far as he ceases to be free and becomes unfree, and this can be brought about in several ways. The first step to be taken is to prevent him for a certain time from returning to his village. Planters and forest-owners never, on principle, hire labourers from the neighbourhood, but engage for a year young men from strange tribes who live at a distance, and then bring them where they are wanted by water. The agreements are drawn up by the Government, and, like many other things in French colonial administration, are calculated to effect their object with due regard to humanity. At the end of each week the labourer is paid half, but only half, of his wages ; the rest is put by and is handed over to him at the end of the year when the white man has to send him home. He is thus prevented from spending his money as quickly as he earns it, and from going home with empty hands. Most of them hire themselves out in this way to get money enough to buy a wife.

And what is the result ? They have to hold out for the year, because they cannot get back to their village, but very few of them are really useful workers. Many get homesick. Others cannot put up with the strange diet, for, as no fresh provisions are to be had, they must as a rule live chiefly on rice. Most of them fall victims to the taste for rum, and ulcers and diseases spread rapidly among them, living, as they do, a kind of barrack life in overcrowded huts. In spite of all precautions they mostly get through their pay as soon as the contract time is up, and return home as poor as they went away.

The negro is worth something only so long as he is in his village and under the moral control of intercourse with his family and other relatives ; away from these surroundings he easily goes to the bad, both morally and physically. Colonies of negro labourers away from their families are, in fact, centres of demoralisation, and yet such colonies are required for trade and for the cultivation of the soil, both of which would be impossible without them.

The tragic element in this question is that the interests of civilisation and of colonisation do not coincide, but are largely antagonistic to each other. The former would be promoted best by the natives being left in their villages and there trained to various industries, to lay out plantations, to grow a little coffee or cocoa for themselves or even for sale, to build themselves houses of timber or brick instead of huts of bamboo, and so to live a steady and worthy life. Colonisation, however, demands that as much of the population as possible shall be made available in every possible way for utilising to the utmost the natural wealth of the country. Its watchword is " Production," so that the capital invested in the colonies may pay its interest, and that the motherland may get her needs supplied through her connection with them. For the unsuspected incompatibilities which show themselves here, no individual is responsible ; they arise out of the circumstances themselves, and the lower the level of the natives and the thinner the population, the harder is the problem. In Zululand, for example, agriculture and cattle raising are possible, and the

natives develop naturally into a peasantry attached to
the land and practising home industries, while, at the
same time, the population is so thick that the labour
requirements of European trade can also be met ;
there, then, the problems of the condition of the natives
and the promotion of civilisation among them are far
less difficult than in the colonies where the country is
mostly virgin forest and the population is at a really
primitive stage of culture.   Yet even there, too, it may
come about that the economic progress aimed at by
colonisation is secured at the expense of civilisation and
the native standard of life.

What, then, is the real educational value of the much
discussed compulsory labour as enforced by the State ?
What is meant by labour compulsion ?

It means that every native who has not some
permanent industry of his own must, by order of the
State, spend so many days in the year in the service of
either a trader or a planter.   On the Ogowe we have
no labour compulsion.   The French colonial administration tries, on principle, to get on without any such
measure.   In German Africa, where labour compulsion
was enforced in a humane but effective manner, the
results were, according to some critics, good ; according
to others, bad.   I myself hold labour compulsion to be
not wrong in principle, but impossible to carry through
in practice.   The average colony cannot get on without
having it on a small scale.   If I were an official and a
planter came to tell me that his labourers had left him
just as the cocoa crop had to be gathered, and that the
men in the neighbouring villages refused to come to his
help at this critical time, I should think I had a right,
and that it was even my duty, to secure him the labour

of these men so long as he needed it for the saving of his crop, on payment, of course, of the wages usual in the locality. But the enforcement of general labour compulsion is complicated by the fact that under it men have practically always to leave their village and their family and go to work many miles away. Who provides their food on the journey ? What becomes of them if they fall ill ? Who will guarantee that the white man does not call on them for their labour just when their village has to set about its own planting, or when it is the best time for fishing expeditions ? Will he not, perhaps, keep them longer than he is entitled to, on the plea that they have done no work ? Will he treat them properly ? There is always the danger that compulsory labour may become, secretly but really, a kind of slavery.

Connected to some extent with the question of compulsory labour is that of the management of colonies by the method of " concessions." What is meant by a " concession " ? A company with plenty of capital has a large stretch of territory assigned to it, which it is to manage for so many years, and no other trader may establish himself there. Competition being thus excluded, the natives become very seriously dependent on the company and its employees. Even if the sovereign rights of the State are reserved to it on paper, the trading company does in practice come to exercise many of them more or less completely, especially if the taxes which are owed to the State can be paid to the company in the form of natural products or of labour, to be handed on by it to the State in the form of cash. The question has been much discussed at times, because the system of large concessions led in the Belgian Congo to great abuses, and I do not ignore its dangers ; it can, if taken advantage of wrongly, lead to the native belonging to the trader or planter as a creature that has no rights. But it has also its good points. The upper course of the Ogowe has been granted as a concession to the " Company of the Upper Ogowe," and I have discussed the question thoroughly with employees of this company who were with me for considerable periods for medical treatment, thus getting to know the arguments of both sides. When a company has not to fear competition, it can— as the " Company of the Upper Ogowe " does—banish rum and cheap spirits from its district, and provide for sale in its stores only things that are worth buying, w thout any rubbish. Directed by men of intelligence and wide views, it can exert much educational influence, and since the land belongs wholly to it for a long period, it has a real interest in seeing that it is managed properly ; and it is little tempted to exhaust the soil.

On the whole, then, the general principle of labour compulsion, in the sense that the State puts the natives at the disposal of private individuals, is to be rejected. The State has to apply it to a quite sufficient extent in the work it has to exact from the natives for generally necessary public objects. It must have at its disposal boatmen and carriers for its officials when they travel ; it must have men in its service for the construction and maintenance of roads, and under certain circumstances it must exact contributions of foodstuffs for the support of its troops and its staff generally.

There are two things which are terribly difficult in Africa : one is to provide any place which has a large population with fresh provisions, and the other is to maintain roads through the forest; and both of these become proportionately more difficult where the population is thin and the distances great. I speak from experience. What trouble I have to secure food for my two assistants and for those of the sick in my hospital who live too far away to get what is necessary sent to them regularly from home! There come times when I have to resort to compulsory measures, and say that every one who comes for treatment must bring a contribution of so many bananas or manioc sticks. This leads to endless wranglings with the patients, who say either that they do not know about the order, or that they have not enough for themselves. Of course, I do treat the serious cases and those who come from long distances, even if they have not brought the modest tribute demanded, but, however strongly I insist on this contribution being made, it does sometimes happen that I have to send sick people away because I no longer have the means of feeding them. The head of the mission station, who has to provide food for the 100 or 150 children in the school, is sometimes in the same position, and the school has to be closed, and the children sent home, because we cannot feed them.

The labour levies and the food requisitions naturally affect chiefly the villages which lie nearest the white settlements. However considerate and just the action of the Government is, these natives feel it, nevertheless, as a burden, and endeavour to migrate to more distant parts, where they will be left in peace. Hence, in the neighbourhoods where there are only primitive tribes, and these not in great numbers, there comes into existence round the settlements of the whites a zone which is uninhabited. Then the compulsion has to be applied in another way. The natives are forbidden to move their villages, and those at a distance are ordered to come near the white settlements, or to move to specified points on the caravan routes or on the river. This must be done, but it is tragic that it should be necessary, and the authorities have to take care that no change is enforced beyond what is really needful.

In the Cameroons the forest has been pierced with a network of roads, which are kept in splendid condition and are the admiration of all visitors from other colonies. But has not this great achievement been brought about at the cost of the native population and their vital interests ? One is forced to ask questions when things have gone so far that women are impressed for the maintenance of the roads. It is impossible to acquiesce when, as is often the case, the colony itself prospers, while the native population diminishes year by year. Then the present is living at the expense of the future, and the obvious fatal result is only a question of time. The maintenance of the native population must be the first object of any sound colonial policy.

*

*   *

Close on the problem of labour comes that of the educated native. Taken by itself, a thorough school education is, in my opinion, by no means necessary for these primitive peoples. The beginning of civilisation with them is not knowledge, but industry and agriculture, through which alone can be secured the economic conditions of higher civilisation. But both Government and trade require natives with extensive knowledge whom they can employ in administration and in the stores. The schools, therefore, must set their aims higher than is natural, and produce people who understand complicated figures and can write the white man's language perfectly. Many a native has such ability that the results of this attempt are, so far as intellectual knowledge goes, astounding. Not long ago there came to me a native Government clerk, just at the time that there was also a missionary staying with me. When the clerk went away, the missionary and I said to each other : " Well, we could hardly compete with him in essay writing ! " His chief gives him documents of the most difficult sort to draw up and most complicated statistics to work out, and he does it all faultlessly.

But what becomes of these people ? They have been uprooted from their villages, just like those who go off to work for strangers. They live at the store, continually exposed to the dangers which haunt every native so closely, the temptations to defraud and to drink. They earn good wages, indeed, but as they have to buy all their necessaries at high prices, and are a prey to the black man's innate love of spending, they often find themselves in financial difficulties and even in want. They do not now belong to the ordinary negroes, nor do they belong to the whites either ; they are a *tertium quid* between the two. Quite recently the above-mentioned Government clerk said to the wife of a missionary : " We negro intellectuals are in a very uncomfortable position. The women in these parts are too uneducated to be good wives for us. They should import wives for us from the higher tribes in Madagascar." This loss of class position in an upwards direction is the misfortune which comes to many of the best of the natives.

Emancipation from the savage state produced by the accumulation of wealth plays no part here, though it may do so in other colonies. It is a still more dangerous method than that of intellectual education.

Social problems are also produced by imports from Europe. Formerly the negroes practised a number of small industries ; they carved good household utensils out of wood ; they manufactured excellent cord out of bark fibre and similar substances ; they got salt from the sea. But these and other primitive industries have been destroyed by the goods which European trade has introduced into the forest. The cheap enamelled ware has driven out the solid, home-made wooden bucket, and round every negro village there arc heaps of such things rusting in the grass. Many minor crafts which they once practised are now almost forgotten ; it is now only the old women who know how to make cord out of bark, and sewing cotton out of the fibres of the pineapple leaves. Even the art of canoe-making is dying out. Thus native industries are going backwards instead of forwards, just when the rise of a solid industrial class would be the first and surest step towards civilisation.

※

※   ※

One first gets a clear idea of the real meaning of the social danger produced by the importation of cheap spirits, when one reads how much rum per head of the population comes every year to the port towns, and when one has seen in the villages how the children drink with their elders. Here on the Ogowe officials and traders, missionaries and chiefs are all unanimous that the importation of cheap spirits should be stopped. Why, then, is it not stopped ? Because it is so profitable to the revenue. The import duty on rum produces one of the biggest items in the receipts of the colony, and if it ceased there would be a deficit. The financial position of the African colonies is well known to be anything but brilliant, and the duty on spirits has a second advantage, that it can be increased every year without diminishing by a litre the quantity consumed. The position here, as in other colonies, is that the Government says : " Abolish cheap spirits ? Willingly— to-day rather than to-morrow ; but tell us first what we can find to cover the deficit which that will cause in the budget." And the strongest opponents of alcohol have not been able to make any practicable proposal. When shall we find some way out of this idiotic dilemma? The one hope is that some day a governor will come who will put the future of the colony above the financial worries of the present, and have the courage to banish rum at the price of having to carry on for some years with a deficit.*

It is often asserted that alcoholism would prevail among the natives even if there were no importation of spirits. This is mere talk. Of alcoholic drinks pro- duced in the country itself palm wine is the only one which has to be considered in the forest, and that is no great danger. It is simply the sap of the palm tree allowed to ferment, but the boring of the trees and the taking the necessary vessels to them needs a good deal of labour, for the work has to be done on the quiet at a

* In the year 1919 the Governor actually ventured to try this policy to the great joy of the whole colony.

distance from the village, the boring of the trees being expressly forbidden. Moreover, palm wine will not keep. Its existence makes it possible, therefore, for the people of a village to get drunk several times a year, on the occasions of their festivals, but it is not a continual danger like the cheap spirits sold in the stores. Fresh palm wine tastes, when it is fermenting, very like the must of grape wine, and by itself it is not any more intoxicating than the latter; but the natives are accustomed to put various species of bark into it, and then it can produce a terrible kind of drunkenness.

Polygamy is another difficult social problem. We Europeans come here with our ideal of monogamy, and missionaries contend with all their resources against polygamy, in some places even urging the Government to suppress it by law. On the other hand, all of us here must allow that it is closely bound up with the existing economic and social conditions. Where the population lives in bamboo huts, and society is not so organised that a woman can earn her own living, there is no room for the unmarried woman, and if all women are to be married, polygamy is a necessary condition. Moreover, there are in the forest neither cows nor nanny goats, so that a mother must suckle her child for a long time if it is to be reared. Polygamy safeguards the claims of the child, for after its birth the woman has the right, and the duty, of living only for her child; she is now no longer a wife, but only a mother, and she often spends the greater part of this time with her parents. At the end of three years comes the weaning, which is marked by a festival, and then she returns to her husband's hut to be a wife once more. But this living for her child is not to be thought of unless the man has another wife, or other wives, to make a home for him and look after his banana plots.

Here is another point for consideration. Among these nature-peoples there are no widows unprovided for and no neglected orphans. The nearest male relative inherits the dead man's widow, and must maintain her and her children. She enters into enjoyment of all the rights of his other wives, even though she can later, with his consent, take another husband.

To agitate, therefore, against polygamy among primitive peoples, is to undermine the whole structure of their society. Have we the right to do this if we are not also in a position to give them a new social order which suits their own circumstances? Were the agitation successful, would not polygamy still continue to exist, with the single difference that the later wives would be illegitimate ones? These questions naturally cause missionaries much anxious thought.

But, as a matter of fact, the more developed the economic condition of a people becomes, the easier becomes the contest with polygamy. When men begin to live in permanent houses, and to practise the rearing of cattle, and agriculture, it disappears of itself because it is no longer demanded by their circumstances, and is no longer even consistent with them. Among the Israelites, as their civilisation advanced, monogamy peacefully drove out polygamy. During the prophetic period they were both practised side by side; the teaching of Jesus does not even hint at the existence of the latter.

Certainly mission teaching should put forward monogamy as the ideal and as what Christianity demands, but it would be a mistake for the State to make it compulsory. It is also a mistake, so far as I can judge, to identify the fight against immorality with that against polygamy. Under this system the relation of the wives to each other is usually good. A negress does not, in fact, like being the only wife, because then she has the care of the banana plot, which always falls to the wives, all to herself, and this is a laborious duty, as the plots are usually at a distance from the village in some well-concealed part of the forest.

What I have seen in my hospital of life with many wives has not shown me, at any rate, the ugly side of the system. An elderly chief once came as a patient and brought two young wives with him. When his condition began to cause anxiety, a third appeared who was considerably older than the first two ; this was his first wife. From the day of her arrival she sat continually on his bed, held his head in her lap, and gave him what he wanted to drink. The two young ones behaved respectfully to her, took orders from her, and looked after the cooking.

One can have the experience in this land of a fourteen-year-old boy announcing himself as a *paterfamilias*. It comes about in the following way. He has inherited from some deceased relative a wife with children, and though the woman has contracted a marriage with another man, that does not touch his rights over the children nor his duty towards them. If they are boys, he will some day have to buy wives for them ; if they are girls, he will get the customary purchase price from those who wish to marry them.

Should one declaim against the custom of wife-purchase, or tolerate it ? If it is a case of a young woman being promised, without being herself consulted, to the man who bids most for her, it is obviously right to protest. If it merely means that in accordance with local custom the man who is courting a girl must, if she is willing to marry him, pay to the family a sum mutually agreed upon, there is no more reason for objecting than there is in the matter of the dowry, customary in Europe. Whether the man, if the marriage comes off, pays money to the family or receives money from it, is in principle the same thing ; in either case there is a definite money transaction which has its origin in the social views of the period. What has to be insisted on, both among ourselves and among " natives," is that the money transaction must remain subordinate, and not so influence the personal choice that either the wife is bought, as in Africa, or the husband, as in Europe. What we have to do, then, is not to fight against the custom of wife-purchase, but to educate the natives up to seeing that they must not give the girl to the highest bidder, but to the suitor who can make her happy, and whom she is herself inclined to take. As a rule, indeed, the negro girls are not so wanting in independence as to let themselves be sold to any one who offers. Love, it is true, does not play the same part in marriage here as with us, for the child of nature knows nothing of the romantic, and marriages are usually decided on in the family council ; they do, however, as a rule, turn out happily.

Most girls are married when they are fifteen, even those in the girls' schools. Those in our mission school are mostly already engaged to some husband, and marry as soon as they leave school. They can even be promised to a husband before they are born, as I learnt through a case of most unprincipled wife-purchase, which took place at Samkita, and was related to me by a missionary. A man owed one of his neighbours £16 (400 fr.), but, instead of repaying it, he bought a wife and married her with the usual ceremonies. While they were at the wedding feast, the creditor made his appearance, and overwhelmed the bridegroom with abuse for having bought a wife instead of paying his debt. A palaver began which ended in an agreement that the debtor should give his creditor the first girl born of the marriage for a wife, on which the latter joined the guests and took his part in the festivities. Sixteen years later he came as a wooer, and so the debt was paid !

My opinion is, and I have formed it after conversation with all the best and most experienced of the white men in this district, that we should accept, but try to improve and refine, the rights and customs which we find in existence, and make no alterations which are not absolutely necessary.

*

*   *

A word in conclusion about the relations between the whites and the blacks. What must be the general character of the intercourse between them ? Am I to treat the black man as my equal or as my inferior ? I must show him that I can respect the dignity of human personality in every one, and this attitude in me he must be able to see for himself ; but the essential thing is that there shall be a real feeling of brotherliness. How far this is to find complete expression in the sayings and doings of daily life must be settled by circumstances. The negro is a child, and with children nothing can be done without the use of authority.   We must, therefore, so arrange the circumstances of daily life that my natural authority can find expression.   With regard to the negroes, then, I have coined the formula : " I am your brother, it is true, but your elder brother."

The combination of friendliness with authority is therefore the great secret of successful intercourse. One of our missionaries, Mr. Robert, left the staff some years ago to live among the negroes as their brother absolutely.   He built himself a small house near a village between Lambarene and N'Gômô, and wished to be recognised as a member of the village.   From that day his life became a misery.   With his abandonment of the social interval between white and black he lost all his influence ; his word was no longer taken as the " white man's word," but he had to argue every point with them as if he were merely their equal.)

When, before coming to Africa, I heard missionaries and traders say again and again that one must be very careful out here to maintain this authoritative position of the white man, it seemed to me to be a hard and unnatural position to take up, as it does to every one in Europe who reads or hears the same.   Now I have come to see that the deepest sympathy and kindness can be combined with this insistence on certain external forms, and indeed are only possible by means of them. One of our unmarried missionaries at N'Gômô—the story belongs to a period some years back—allowed his cook to be very free in his behaviour towards him.   One day the steamer put in with the Governor on board, and the missionary went to pay his respects to the high official.   He was standing on deck in an elegant suit of white among a group of officials and military men,

when a negro, with his cap on his head and a pipe in
his mouth, pushed himself into the group and said to
him : " Well, what are we to have for supper to-
night ? " The cook wanted to show on what good
terms he stood with his master !

The prevention of unsuitable freedom is, however,
only the external and technical part, so to say, of the
problem of authority. ⟨A white man can only have
real authority if the native respects him.⟩ No one must
imagine that the child of nature looks up to us merely
because we know more, or can do more, than he can.
This superiority is so obvious to him that it ceases to
be taken into account. It is by no means the case that
the white man is to the negro an imposing person
because he possesses railways and steamers, can fly in
the air, or travel under water. " White people are
clever and can do anything they want to," says Joseph.
The negro is not in a position to estimate what these
technical conquests of nature mean as proofs of mental
and spiritual superiority, but on one point he has an
unerring intuition, and that is on the question whether
any particular white man is a real, moral personality
or not. If the native feels that he is this, moral
authority is possible ; if not, it is simply impossible to
create it. The child of nature, not having been
artificialised and spoilt as we have been, has only
elementary standards of judgment, and he measures us
by the most elementary of them all, the moral standard.
Where he finds goodness, justice, and genuineness of
character, real worth and dignity, that is, behind the
external dignity given by social circumstances, he bows
and acknowledges his master ; where he does not find
them he remains really defiant in spite of all appearance

ON THE BANK OF THE OGOWE RIVER.

of submission, and says to himself : " This white is no more of a man than I am, for he is not a better one than I am."

I am not thinking merely of the fact that many un-suitable, and not a few quite unworthy men, go out into the colonies of all nations. I wish to emphasise a further fact that even the morally best and the idealists find it difficult out here to be what they wish to be. We all get exhausted in the terrible contest between the European worker who bears the responsi-bility and is always in a hurry, and the child of nature who does not know what responsibility is and is never in a hurry. The Government official has to record at the end of the year so much work done by the native in building and in road-maintenance, in service as carrier or boatman, and so much money paid in taxes ; the trader and the planter are expected by their com-panies to provide so much profit for the capital invested in the enterprise. But in all this they are for ever dependent on men who cannot share the responsibility that weighs on them, who only give just so much return of labour as the others can force out of them, and who if there is the slightest failure in superintendence, do exactly as they like without any regard for the loss that may be caused to their employers. In this daily and hourly contest with the child of nature every white man is continually in danger of gradual moral ruin.

My wife and I were once very much delighted with a newly-arrived trader, because in the conversations we had with him he was always insisting on kindness to-wards the natives, and would not allow the slightest ill-treatment of them by his foremen. The next spring, however, he had the following experience. Lying in a pond some sixty miles from here he had a large quantity of mahogany, but he was summoned to Lambarene to clear off some urgent correspondence just as the water began to rise. He ordered his foremen and labourers to be sure to use the two or three days of high water to get all the timber, if possible, into the river. When the water had fallen he went back to the place and found that nothing whatever had been done! They had smoked, and drunk, and danced; the timber which had already lain too long in the pond was almost completely ruined, and he was responsible to his company for the loss. His men had been thoughtless and indifferent because they did not fear him enough. This experience changed him entirely, and now he laughs at those who think it is possible to do anything with the natives without employing relentless severity.

Not long ago the termites, or white ants, got into a box which stood on our verandah. I emptied the box and broke it up, and gave the pieces to the negro who had been helping me. " Look," I said to him, " the ants have got into it; you mustn't put the wood with the rest of the firewood or the ants will get into the framework of the hospital building. Go down to the river and throw it into the water. Do you understand?" " Yes, yes, you need not worry." It was late in the day, and being too tired to go down the hill again, I was inclined to break my general rule and trust a black —one who was in fact on the whole intelligent and handy. But about ten o'clock I felt so uneasy that I took the lantern and went down to the hospital. There was the wood with the ants in it lying with the rest of the firewood. To save himself the trouble of going the twenty yards down to the river the negro had endangered all my buildings !

The greater the responsibility that rests on a white man, the greater the danger of his becoming hard towards the natives. We on a mission staff are too easily inclined to become self-righteous with regard to the other whites. We have not got to obtain such and such results from the natives by the end of the year, as officials and traders have, and therefore this exhausting contest is not so hard a one for us as for them. I no longer venture to judge my fellows after learning something of the soul of the white man who is in business from those who lay as patients under my roof, and whose talk has led me to suspect that those who now speak savagely about the natives may have come out to Africa full of idealism, but in the daily contest have become weary and hopeless, losing little by little what they once possessed of spirituality.

That it is so hard to keep oneself really humane, and so to be a standard-bearer of civilisation, that is the tragic element in the problem of the relations between white and coloured men in Equatorial Africa.

CHAPTER VIII

A war-Christmas in the virgin forest ! When the
candles on the little palm which served us as Christmas
tree had burnt to half their length I blew them out.
" What are you doing ? " asked my wife. " They are
all we have," said I, " and we must keep them for next
year." " For next year ? " . . . and she shook her
head.

On August 4th, two days after our return from Cape
Lopez, I had prepared some medicine for a lady who
was ill there, and sent Joseph to a store to ask that their
steamer might take the packet down there on its next
journey. He brought back a short note : " In Europe
they are mobilising and probably already at war. We
must place our steamer at the disposal of the authorities,
and cannot say when it will go next to Cape Lopez."

We needed days to realise that Europe was at war,
though it was not that we had failed to take the possi-
bility of it into account ; indeed, following the advice
of an experienced merchant, I had brought with me a
considerable sum in metal money in case it should come
about. But since the beginning of July we had received no news from Europe, and we knew nothing of
the entanglements which finally brought on the fatal
explosion.

The negroes had, at first, very little understanding of

what was going on. The Catholics among them were more really interested in the papal election than in the war, during the autumn. " Doctor," said Joseph to me during a canoe journey, " how do the Cardinals really elect the Pope ; do they take the oldest one, or the most religious, or the cleverest ? " " They take one kind of man this time, and another kind the next, according to circumstances," was my reply.

At first the black labourers felt the war as by no means a misfortune, as for several weeks very few were impressed for service. The whites did little but sit together and discuss the news and the rumours from Europe. By now, however (Christmas, 1914), the coloured folk are beginning to learn that the war has consequences which affect them also. There being a shortage of ships, no timber can be exported, and therefore the labourers from a distance who had been engaged for a year are being discharged by the stores, and as, further, there are no vessels plying on the rivers that could take them back to their homes, they collect in groups and try to reach the Loango coast, from which most of them come, on foot.

Again, a sudden rise in the price of tobacco, sugar, rice, kerosene, and rum, brings home to the negro's consciousness the fact that there is a war going on, and this rise is what gives them more concern than anything else for the moment. Not long ago, while we were bandaging patients, Joseph began to complain of the war, as he had several times done before, as the cause of this rise in prices, when I said to him : " Joseph, you mustn't talk like that. Don't you see how troubled the faces of the doctor and his wife are, and the faces of all the missionaries ? For us the war means very

K

much more than an unpleasant rise in prices.   We are,
all of us, anxious about the lives of so many of our dear
fellow-men, and we can hear from far away the groaning
of the wounded and the death rattle of the dying."   He
looked up at me with great astonishment at the time,
but since then I have noticed that he now seems to see
something that was hidden from him before.

We are, all of us, conscious that many natives are
puzzling over the question how it can be possible that
the whites, who brought them the Gospel of Love, are
now murdering each other, and throwing to the winds
the commands of the Lord Jesus.   When they put the
question to us we are helpless.   If I am questioned on
the subject by negroes who think, I make no attempt
to explain or to extenuate, but say that we are in
" front " of something terrible and incomprehensible.
How far the ethical and religious authority of the white
man among these children of nature is impaired by this
war we shall only be able to measure later on.   I fear
that the damage done will be very considerable.

In my own house I take care that the blacks learn as
little as possible of the horrors of war.   The illustrated
papers we receive—for the post has begun to work
again fairly regularly—I must not leave about, lest the
boys, who can read, should absorb both text and
pictures and retail them to others.

Meanwhile the medical work goes on as usual.
Every morning when I go down to the hospital I feel
it as an inexpressible mercy that, while so many men
find it their duty to inflict suffering and death on others,
I can be doing good and helping to save human life.
This feeling supports me through all my weariness.

The last ship which left Europe before the declaration

of war brought me several cases of drugs and two of bandages, the last a gift from a lady supporter, so that I am now provided with what is necessary for carrying on the hospital for some months. The goods for Africa which were not sent by this vessel are still lying on the quays of Havre and Bordeaux. Who knows when they will arrive, or whether they will get here at all ?

*

*   *

I am worried, however, about how to provide food for the sick, for there is something like a famine in the district—thanks to the elephants ! People in Europe usually imagine that where " civilisation " comes, the wild animals begin to die out. That may be the case in many districts, but in others the very opposite happens, and that for three reasons. First, if, as is often the case, the native population diminishes, there is less hunting done. Secondly, what hunting is done is less successful, for the natives have forgotten how to trap the animals in the primitive but often extremely ingenious manner of their ancestors, and have got accustomed to hunting them with firearms. But in view of eventual possibilities it has been for years the policy of all Governments in Equatorial Africa to allow the natives only small quantities of gunpowder ; nor may they possess modern sporting guns ; they can only have the old flintlocks. Thirdly, the war on the wild animals is carried on much less energetically because the natives no longer have the time to devote to it. At timber felling and rafting they earn more money than they can by hunting, so that the elephants flourish and increase in numbers almost unhindered, and the results of this we are now beginning to

experience. The banana plantations of the villages
north-west from here, which provide us with so much
of our food, are continually visited by elephants.
Twenty of these creatures are enough to lay waste a
whole plantation in a night, and what they do not eat
they trample underfoot.

It is not, however, to the plantations only that the
elephants are a danger. The telegraph line from
N'Djôle to the interior knows something about the
damage they do. The long, straight clearing through
the forest which marks its course is in itself a tremendous
attraction to the animals, but the straight, smooth
telegraph poles are irresistible. They seem to have
been provided expressly for pachyderms to rub themselves against ! They are not all very firm, and a
very little rubbing brings one of the weaker ones to
the ground, but there is always another like it not very
far off. Thus, in a single night one strong elephant
can bring down a big stretch of telegraph line, and days
may pass before the occupants of the nearest guard
station have discovered the damage and repaired it.

Although the elephants that roam the neighbourhood
cause me so much anxiety about the feeding of my
patients, I have not yet seen one, and very probably
never shall. During the day they stay in unap-
proachable swamps in order to sally out at night and
plunder the plantations which they have reconnoitred
beforehand. A native who is here for the treatment of
his wife, who has heart complaint, is a clever wood-
carver, and carved me an elephant. Though I admired
this work of primitive art, I ventured to remark that he
seemed not to have got the body quite right. The
artist, insulted, shrugged his shoulders. " Do you

A MISSIONARY'S BUNGALOW AT LAMBARENE.

THE BOYS' SCHOOL AT LAMBARENE.

think you can teach me what an elephant looks like ? I once had one on top of me, trying to trample me underfoot." The artist was, in fact, also a famous elephant hunter. Their method now is to go out by day and creep to within ten paces of the elephant, when they discharge their flintlock at him. If the shot is not fatal and they are discovered by the animal, they are then, of course, in a very unpleasant position.

Hitherto I have been able to help out the feeding of my sick with rice, if bananas were short, but I can do so no more. What we still have left we must keep for ourselves, for whether we shall get any more from Europe is more than questionable.

CHAPTER IX

CHRISTMAS, 1915

CHRISTMAS again in the forest, but again a war Christmas! The candle ends which we saved from last year have been used up on our this year's Christmas (palm) tree.

It was a year of difficulties, with a great deal of extra work during the early months. Heavy rainstorms had undermined the spot on which the largest hospital ward stood, so that I had to decide to build a wall round it, and also to lay stone gutters throughout the hospital to carry off the water which streamed from the hill just above it. This needed a number of stones, some of them big ones, and these were either fetched by canoe or rolled down from the hill; but I had always to be on the spot, and often to lend a hand. Our next object was the wall, for which we got help from a native who knew something about building, and we fortunately had on the station a cask of half-spoilt cement. In four months the work was finished.

I was hoping now to have a little rest, when I discovered that, in spite of all our precautions, the termites had got into the chests where we kept our store of drugs and bandages. This necessitated the opening and unpacking of the cases, a work which occupied all our spare time for weeks. Fortunately, I had noticed them in good time, or the damage done

would have been much greater ; but the peculiar
delicate smell, like that of burning, which the termites
produce, had attracted my attention.   Externally there
was no sign of them ; the invasion had been made
from the floor through a tiny hole, and from the first
case they had eaten their way into the others which
stood by and upon it.   They had apparently been
attracted by a bottle of medicinal syrup, the cork of
which had got loose.

   Oh, the fight that has to be carried on in Africa with
creeping insects ! What time one loses over the
thorough precautions that have to be taken !   And with
what helpless rage one has to confess again and again
that one has been outwitted !   My wife learnt how to
solder, in order to be able to close up the flour and
maize in tins, but it sometimes happens that you find
swarms of the terrible little weevils (French *charan-
çons*) even in the soldered tins.   The maize for the
fowls they soon reduce to dust.

   Very much dreaded here, too, are small scorpions
and other poisonous insects.   One learns to be so
careful that one never puts one's hand straight into a
drawer or a box as in Europe.   The eyes must precede
the hand.

   Another serious enemy is the traveller ant, which
belongs to the genus *Dorylus*, and from it we suffer a
great deal.   On their great migrations they march
five or six abreast in perfect order, and I once watched
a column near my house which took thirty-six hours
to march past.   If their course is over open ground
and they have to cross a path, the warriors form up
in several rows on either side and with their large jaws
form a kind of palisade to protect the procession, in

which the ordinary traveller ants are carrying the young ones with them. In forming the palisade the warriors turn their backs to the procession—like the Cossacks when protecting the Czar—and in that position they remain for hours at a time.

As a rule there are three or four columns marching abreast of each other, but independently, from five to fifty yards apart. All at once they break up the column and disperse, though how the word of command is given we do not yet know. Anyhow, in the twinkling of an eye a huge area is covered with a quivering, black mass, and every living thing upon it is doomed. Even the great spiders in the trees cannot escape, for these terrible ravagers creep after them in crowds up to the very highest twigs ; and if the spiders, in despair, jump from the trees, they fall victims to the ants on the ground. It is a horrible sight. The militarism of the forest will very nearly bear comparison with that of Europe !

Our house lies on one of the main routes of the traveller ants, which swarm mostly during the night. A peculiar scratching and clucking of the fowls gives us warning of the danger, and then there is no time to be lost. I jump out of bed, run to the fowl-house, and open the door, through which the birds rush out. Shut in, they would inevitably be the prey of the ants, which creep into their mouths and nostrils until they are suffocated, and then devour them, so that in a short time nothing is left but their white bones. The chickens usually fall victims to the robbers ; the fowls can defend themselves till help comes.

Meanwhile my wife has taken the bugle from the wall and blown it three times, which is the signal for

N.'Kendju and some men from the hospital to bring bucketfuls of water from the river. When they arrive, the water is mixed with lysol, and the ground all round the house and under it is sprinkled. While we are doing this we get very badly treated by the warriors, for they creep over us and bite us vigorously; I once counted nearly fifty on me. They bite themselves so firmly in with their jaws that one cannot pull them off. If one tries to do so the body comes away, but the jaws remain in the flesh and have to be taken out separately afterwards. At last the ants move on, leaving thousands of corpses in the puddles, for they cannot stand the smell of the lysol; and so ends the little drama which we have been playing in the darkness, with no light but that of the lantern which my wife has been holding. Once we were attacked by them three times in one week, and Mr. Coillard, the missionary, records in his memoirs, which I am just now reading, that he, too, suffered severely from them in the Zambesi district.

The most extensive migrations of these ants take place at the beginning and end of the rainy season, and between these two periods there is much less reason to expect an attack. As to size, these ants are not much bigger than our European red ones, but their jaws are much more strongly developed, and they march at a much greater speed, a difference which I have noticed as being common to all species of African ants.

*

*   *

Joseph has left me. Being cut off from Strasbourg, the source of my funds, and obliged to contract debts, I found myself compelled to reduce his wages from

70 francs to 35 francs, telling him I had decided on this only from extreme necessity. Nevertheless, he gave me notice, adding that " his dignity would not allow him to serve me for so small a sum." He lives with his parents on the opposite bank of the river, and had been keeping a money-box with a view to the purchase of a wife. This had now to be opened, and it contained nearly £8 (200 francs), but in a few weeks it had all been frittered away.

Now I have to depend only on N'Kendju's help. He is quite handy and useful, except on the days when he is out of temper, when nothing can be done with him ; but in any case I have to do a good many things that Joseph used to do.

In the treatment of ulcers and suppurating wounds I have found pure methylen-violet most useful. This is a drug which is known to the trade as Merk's Pyoktanin. The credit of having made the decisive experiments regarding the disinfecting power of concentrated dyestuffs belongs to Professor Stilling, of Strasbourg, a specialist in diseases of the eye. He placed at my disposal a quantity of Pyoktanin which had been prepared under his superintendence—so that I might test it here—and it reached me not long before the outbreak of war. I began its use with some prejudice against it, but the results are such that I gladly put up with the unpleasant colour. Methylen-violet has the peculiarity of killing the bacteria without affecting or injuring the tissues or being in the least degree poisonous ; in this respect it is much superior to corrosive sublimate, carbolic acid, or tincture of iodine. For the doctor in the forest it is indispensable. Besides this, Pyoktanin does, so far as my observation goes, promote in a striking way the growth of new skin when ulcers are healing.

Before the war I had begun to make a small charge for the medicine to those patients who seemed not to be absolutely poor, and this brought in something like 200 francs (£8) a month. Even though it was only a fraction of the real value of the medicines dispensed, it was something. Now there is no money in the country, and I have to treat the natives almost entirely for nothing.

Of the whites, many who have been prevented by the war from going home have now been four or five years under the equator and are thoroughly exhausted, so that they have to resort to the doctor " for repairs," as we say on the Ogowe. Such patients are sometimes with us for weeks, coming often two and three together. Then I let them use my bedroom and sleep myself in a part of the verandah which has been protected from mosquitoes by wire-netting. That is, however, no great self-denial, for there is more air there than inside. The recovery of the patients is often due much less to my medicines than to the excellent invalid diet provided by the doctor's wife—fortunately we still have a good supply of tins of condensed milk for our patients—and I have for some time had to take care that sick people do not come up here from Cape Lopez for the sake of the diet instead of letting themselves be treated by the doctor there—when there is one. With many of my patients I have become quite intimate, and from conversation with those who stay here a long time I am always learning something fresh about the country and the problem of its colonisation.

*

●   ●

Our own health is not first-class, though it is not really bad ; tropical anæmia has, indeed, already set in. It shows itself in the way the slightest exertion tires one ; I am quite exhausted, for example, after coming up the hill to my house, a matter of four minutes' walk. We also perceive in ourselves a symptom that accompanies it, an excessive nervousness, and besides these two things we find that our teeth are in a bad condition. My wife and I put temporary fillings into each other's teeth, and in this way I give her some relief, but no one can do for me what is really necessary, for that means the removal of two carious teeth which are too far gone to be saved. What stories could be told of toothache in the forest ! One white man whom I know was in such pain, a few years ago, that he could hold out no longer. " Wife," he cried, " get me the small pincers from the tool-chest." Then he lay down, his wife knelt on his chest and got hold of the tooth as well as she could. The man put his hands on hers and together they got out the tooth, which was kind enough to let this treatment be successful.

My mental freshness I have, strange to say, pre-served almost completely in spite of anæmia and fatigue. If the day has not been too exhausting I can give a couple of hours after supper to my studies in ethics and civilisation as part of the history of human thought, any books I need for it and have not with me being sent me by Professor Strohl, of Zürich University. Strange, indeed, are the surroundings amid which I study ; my table stands inside the lattice-door which leads on to the verandah, so that I may snatch as much as possible of the light evening breeze. The palms rustle an *obbligato* to the loud music of the crickets and the toads, and from the forest come harsh and terrifying cries of all sorts. Caramba, my faithful dog, growls gently on the verandah, to let me know that he is there, and at my feet, under the table, lies a small dwarf antelope. In this solitude I try to set in order thoughts which have been stirring in me since 1900, in the hope of giving some little help to the restoration of civilisation. Solitude of the primeval forest, how can I ever thank you enough for what you have been to me ? . . .

The hour between lunch and the resumption of work in the hospital is given to music, as is also Sunday afternoon, and here, too, I feel the blessing of working " far from the madding crowd," for there are many of J. S. Bach's organ pieces into the meaning of which I can now enter with greater ease and deeper appreciation than ever before.

Mental work one must have, if one is to keep one's self in moral health in Africa ; hence the man of culture, though it may seem a strange thing to say, can stand life in the forest better than the uneducated man, because he has a means of recreation of which the other knows nothing. When one reads a good book on a serious subject one is no longer the creature that has been exhausting itself the whole day in the contest with the unreliability of the natives and the tiresome worry of the insects ; one becomes once more a man ! Woe to him who does not in some such way pull himself together and gather new strength ; the terrible prose of African life will bring him to ruin ! Not long ago I had a visit from a white timber merchant, and when I accompanied him to the canoe on his departure I asked him whether I could not provide him with something to read on the two days' journey in front of him. " Many

thanks," he replied, " but I am already supplied," and
he showed me, lying on the thwart of the boat, a book,
which was Jacob Boehme's " Aurora." The work of
the great German shoemaker and mystic, written at
the beginning of the seventeenth century, accompanies
him on all his journeys. We know how nearly all
great African travellers have taken with them solid
matter for reading.

*

*   *

Newspapers one can hardly bear to look at. The
printed string of words, written with a view to the
single, quickly-passing day, seems here, where time is,
so to say, standing still, positively grotesque. Whether
we will or no, all of us here live under the influence of
the daily repeated experience that nature is everything
and man is nothing. This brings into our general view
of life—and this even in the case of the less educated—
something which makes us conscious of the feverishness
and vanity of the life of Europe ; it seems almost
something abnormal that over a portion of the earth's
surface nature should be nothing and man everything !

News of the war comes here fairly regularly. Either
from N'Djôle, through which passes the main telegraph line from Libreville to the interior, or from Cape
Lopez, telegraphic news comes to us every fortnight, a
selection from the various daily items. It is sent by
the District Commandant to the stores and the two
mission stations by means of a native soldier, who waits
till we have read it and give it back to him. Then for
another fortnight we think of the war only in the most

general way. What the frame of mind must be of those who have to go through the excitement of reading war news every day we can hardly imagine. Certainly we do not envy them !

About this time it became known that of the whites who had gone home to fulfil their military duties ten had already been killed, and it made a great impression on the natives. " Ten men killed already in this war ! " said an old Pahouin. " Why, then, don't the tribes meet for a palaver ? How can they pay for all these dead men ? " For, with the natives, it is a rule that all who fall in a war, whether on the victorious or on the defeated side, must be paid for by the other side.

Directly the post has come in, Aloys, my cook, stops me to ask : " Doctor, is it still war ? " " Yes, Aloys, still war." Then he shakes his head sadly and says to himself several times : " Oh, lala ! Oh, lala ! " He is one of the negroes whose soul is really saddened by the thought of the war.

Now we have to be very economical with our European foodstuffs, and potatoes have become a delicacy. A short time ago a white neighbour sent me by his boy a present of several dozen, from which I inferred that he was not well and would soon be needing my services, and so it turned out ! Since the war we have trained ourselves to eat monkey flesh. One of the missionaries on the station keeps a black huntsman, and sends us regularly some of his booty ; it is monkeys that he shoots most frequently, since they are the game he finds easiest to bring down. Their flesh tastes some-thing like goat's flesh, but has a kind of sweetish taste that the latter has not. People may think what they like about Darwinism and the descent of man, but the

prejudice against monkey flesh is not so easily got rid
of. " Doctor," said a white man to me a few days ago,
" eating monkeys is the first step in cannibalism " !

At the end of the summer (1916) we were able to join
our missionary neighbours, Mr. and Mrs. Morel, of
Samkita, in a visit of some weeks to Cape Lopez,
where a trading company, several of whose employees
had benefited by our treatment and hospitality during
illness, placed three rooms in one of their stores at our
disposal. The sea air worked wonders for our health.

CHAPTER X

THE MISSION

July, 1916.

It is the dry season. Every evening we go for a walk on the big sandbanks in the river bed and enjoy the breeze which is blowing upstream. The hospital is not so busy as usual at this season, for the villagers are occupied with their great fishing expeditions, and will not bring me any patients till they are over. So I will make use of these vacant hours to note down the impressions I have formed about the mission. What do I really think about mission work after three years on a mission station?

What does the forest dweller understand of Christianity, and how does he understand—or misunderstand—it? In Europe I met the objection again and again that Christianity is something too high for primitive man, and it used to disturb me; now, as a result of my experience, I can boldly declare, " No ; it is not."

First, let me say that the child of nature thinks a great deal more than is generally supposed. Even though he can neither read nor write, he has ideas on many more subjects than we imagine. Conversations I have had in the hospital with old natives about the ultimate things of life have deeply impressed me. The distinction between white and coloured, educated and uneducated, disappears when one gets talking with the forest dweller about our relations to each other, to mankind, to the universe, and to the infinite. "The negroes are deeper than we are," a white man once said to me, "because they don't read newspapers," and the paradox has some truth in it.

They have, then, a great natural capacity for taking in the elements of religion, though the historical element in Christianity lies, naturally, outside their ken. The negro lives with a general view of things which is innocent of history, and he has no means of measuring and appreciating the time-interval between Jesus and ourselves. Similarly, the doctrinal statements which explain how the divine plan of redemption was prepared and effected, are not easily made intelligible to him, even though he has an elementary consciousness of what redemption is. Christianity is for him the light that shines amid the darkness of his fears ; it assures him that he is not in the power of nature-spirits, ancestral spirits, or fetishes, and that no human being has any sinister power over another, since the will of God really controls everything that goes on in the world.

> " I lay in cruel bondage,
>   Thou cam'st and mad'st me free ! "

These words from Paul Gerhardt's Advent hymn express better than any others what Christianity means for primitive man. That is again and again the thought that fills my mind when I take part in a service on a mission station.

It is well known that hopes and fears about a world beyond play no part in the religion of primitive man ; the child of nature does not fear death, but regards it merely as something natural. The more mediæval

form of Christianity which keeps anxiety about a judgment to come in the foreground, has fewer points of contact with his mentality than the more ethical form.   To
him Christianity is the moral view of life and the world,
which was revealed by Jesus; it is a body of teaching
about the kingdom of God and the grace of God.

Moreover, there slumbers within him an ethical
rationalist.   He has a natural responsiveness to the
notion of goodness and all that is connected with it in
religion.   Certainly, Rousseau and the illuminati of
that age idealised the child of nature, but there was
nevertheless truth in their views about him—in their
belief, that is, in his possession of high moral and
rational capacities.   No one must think that he has
described the thought-world of the negro when he has
made a full list of all the superstitious ideas which he
has taken over, and the traditional legal rules of his
tribe.   They do not form his whole universe, although
he is controlled by them.   There lives within him a dim
suspicion that a correct view of what is truly good
must be attainable as the result of reflection.   In proportion as he becomes familiar with the higher moral
ideas of the religion of Jesus, he finds utterance for
something in himself that has hitherto been dumb, and
something that has been tightly bound up finds release.
The longer I live among the Ogowe negroes, the clearer
this becomes to me.

Thus redemption through Jesus is experienced by
him as a two-fold liberation ; his view of the world is
purged of the previously dominant element of fear, and
it becomes ethical instead of unethical.   Never have I
felt so strongly the victorious power of what is simplest
in the teaching of Jesus as when, in the big schoolroom

at Lambarene, which serves as a church as well, I have
been explaining the Sermon on the Mount, the parables
of the Master, and the sayings of St. Paul about the new
life in which we live.

*

*   *

But now, how far does the negro, as a Christian, really
become another man ?   At his baptism he has re-
nounced all superstition, but superstition is so woven
into the texture of his own life and that of the society
in which he lives, that it cannot be got rid of in twenty-
four hours ; he falls again and again in big things as in
small.   I think, however, that we can take too seriously
the customs and practices from which he cannot set
himself entirely free ; the important thing is to make
him understand that nothing—no evil spirit—really
exists behind his heathenism.

If a child enters the world in our hospital its mother
and itself are both painted white all over face and body
so as to make them look terrifying, a custom which is
found in practice among almost all primitive peoples.
The object is to either frighten or to deceive the evil
spirits which on such an occasion have a special opportunity of being dangerous.   I do not worry myself
about this usage ; I even say sometimes, as soon as the
child is born : " Take care you don't forget the painting ! "   There are times when a little friendly irony is
more dangerous to the spirits and the fetishes than zeal
expended on a direct attack upon them.   I venture to
remind my readers that we Europeans, ourselves, have
many customs which, although we never think about it,
had their origin in heathen ideas.

The ethical conversion, also, is often incomplete with

a negro, but in order to be just to such a convert one must distinguish between the real morality which springs from the heart, and the respectable morality of society; it is wonderful how faithful he often is to the former. One must live among them to know how much it means when a man, because he is a Christian, will not wreak the vengeance which he is expected to take, or even the blood revenge which is thought to be an obligation on him. On the whole I feel that the primitive man is much more good natured than we Europeans are; with Christianity added to his good qualities wonderfully noble characters can result. I expect I am not the only white man who feels himself put to shame by the natives.

But to give up the common habit of lying and the readiness to steal, and to become a more or less reliable man in our sense, is something different from practising the religion of love. If I may venture on a paradox, I would say that the converted native is a moral man more often than he is an honourable one. Still, little can be effected by condemnatory expressions. We must see to it that we put as few temptations as possible in the way of the coloured Christian.

But there are native Christians who are in every respect thoroughly moral personalities; I meet one such every day. It is Ojembo, the teacher in our boys' school, whose name means "the song"; I look upon him as one of the finest men that I know anywhere.

How is it that traders and officials so often speak so unfavourably of native Christians? On my very first journey up the river I learnt from two fellow travellers that they never, on principle, engage any Christian "boys." The fact is that Christianity is considered

responsible for the unfavourable phenomena of intellectual emancipation. The young Christians have
mostly been in our mission schools, and get into the
difficult position which for the native is so often bound
up with a school education. They think themselves
too good for many kinds of work, and will no longer be
treated as ordinary negroes. I have experienced this
with some of my own boys. One of them, Atombogunjo
by name, who was in the first class at N'Gômô, worked
for me once during the school holidays. On the very
first day, while he was washing up on the verandah, he
stuck up a school book, open, before him. " What a
fine boy! What keenness for learning ! " said my wife.
Ultimately, however, we found that the open school
book meant something beyond a desire for knowledge ;
it was also a symbol of independence intended to show
us that the fifteen-year-old youth was too good for
ordinary service, and was no longer willing to be treated
as a mere " boy," like other " boys." Finally, I could
stand his conceit no longer, and put him unceremoniously
outside the door.

Now in the colonies almost all schools are mission
schools—the Governments establish hardly any, but
leave the work to the missions—so that all the unhealthy
phenomena which accompany intellectual emancipation
show themselves among the scholars and are therefore
put down as the fault of Christianity. The whites,
however, often forget what they owe to the missions.
Once, when, on board the steamer, the manager of a
large company began to abuse the missions in my
presence, I asked him : " Where, then, did the black
clerks and the black store employees who work for you,
get their education ? To whom do you owe it that you

can find natives here on the Ogowe who can read, write,
and handle figures, and who are to a certain extent
reliable ? " He had no reply to make to that.

*

*   *

But how is a mission carried on ? With what must
it be provided, and how does it work ? In Europe
many people picture it as a sort of village parsonage set
down in the virgin forest, but it is something much
more comprehensive than that, and more complicated
too ; it may be said to be the seat of a bishop, an
educational centre, a farming establishment, and a
market !

In an ordinary mission station there must be one
missionary as head, another for the mission work in the
district, a man to teach in the boys' school, and a
woman for the girls' school, with one or two practical
workers, and, if possible, a doctor. Only a mission
station of that size can accomplish anything worth
mentioning ; an incomplete one only uses up men and
money with no permanent result.

As an illustration of this take Talagonga, where at
the beginning of my time here there was a splendid
evangelist working, Mr. Ford, an American, but the
station had no practical workers. There came a time
when it was absolutely necessary to repair the floor of
the house, built upon piles, in which Mr. and Mrs. Ford
and their children lived, because mosquitoes found their
way in through the holes in it, and, as fever carriers,
endangered the lives of the inmates. So Mr. Ford set
to work at the job and finished it in about two months,
during which time the neighbourhood was left without
any spiritual direction. A practical worker would have

done it all in three weeks and made a permanent job of it, not mere temporary patchwork. This is one example out of hundreds of the useless, unprofitable condition of insufficiently manned mission stations.

In the tropics a man can do at most half of what he can manage in a temperate climate. If he is dragged about from one task to another he gets used up so quickly that, though he is still on the spot, the working capacity he represents is *nil*. Hence a strict division of labour is absolutely necessary, though on the other hand, each member must be able, when circumstances demand it, to turn his hand to anything. A missionary who does not understand something of practical work, of garden work, of treatment of the sick, is a misfortune to a mission station.

The missionary who is there for the evangelistic work must as a rule have nothing to do with the carrying on of the daily work of the station ; he must be free to undertake every day his longer or shorter journeys for the purpose of visiting the villages, nor must he be obliged to be back at the mission on a particular day. He may be invited while out on one of his journeys to go to this or that village which was not included in his plan, because the people there want to hear the Gospel. He must never answer that he has no time, but must be able to give them two or three days or even a whole week. When he gets back he must rest, for an unbroken fortnight on the river or on forest paths will certainly have exhausted him.

Too few missionary journeys, and those too hastily carried through, that is the miserable mistake of almost all missions, and the cause of it always is that in consequence of an insufficient number of workers or of unwise division of work, the evangelist takes part in the superintendence of the station, and the Head of the station goes travelling.

On the Head of the station falls the work of the services in the station and in the nearest villages, together with the superintendence of the schools and of the cultivated land. He ought really never to leave the station for a day ; he must have his eyes everywhere, and any one ought to be able to speak to him at any time. His most prosaic business is conducting the market. The foodstuffs which we need for the school children, the labourers, and the boatmen of the station, we do not have to buy with money. Only when the natives know that they can get satisfactory goods of all sorts from us, do they bring us regular supplies of manioc, bananas, and dried fish; so the mission must have a shop. Two or three times a week the natives come with the product of their plots and with fish, and barter what they have brought for salt, nails, kerosene, fishing materials, tobacco, saws, knives, axes, and cloth. We do not supply rum or spirits. This takes up the Head's whole morning, and then what a time it takes him in addition to send off his European orders correctly and at the right time, to keep the accounts accurately, to pay the boatmen and the labourers their wages, and to look after all the cultivated ground ! What losses are entailed, too, if he fails to have necessary material in hand when it is wanted ! A roof has to be put on, and there are no raffia leaves ready, dried and sewn into sheets ; there is some building to be done, and there are no beams and no boards ; or the best time for brickmaking has been allowed to pass unused ; or he has postponed too long the re-smoking of the store of dried fish for the school children, and discovers one morning that it is all a mass of worms and good for nothing ! It all depends on the Head whether the mission station does its work cheaply and successfully, or expensively and unsuccessfully.

On one of our stations, for example, there had been for several years a succession of Heads who knew but little about land cultivation, and had not pruned the coffee bushes properly. They had let them grow so tall that they no longer produced what they ought to have done, and ladders had to be used to gather the crop. Then it was necessary to cut them off just above the ground, and it will be years before they have produced new shoots which bear a normal crop.

Another of the Head's duties is to investigate the not infrequent cases of theft, in which matter he has more opportunity than he likes for developing whatever detective talent he may possess. He has also to straighten out all the disputes between the coloured inhabitants of the settlement, and in this he must never show any impatience. For hours together he must listen attentively to their barren argumentations, since otherwise he is not the upright judge according to their notions. If canoes come from another station he must entertain and feed the rowers. If the steamer's siren sounds, he must be off with canoes to the landing place to take charge of the mail and the cases of goods.

Again, it may happen that there has been too small a supply of foodstuffs brought in on a market day; this means that canoes must be sent off to the more distant villages to secure what is needed. The expedition may take two or three days ; what work is to be left undone because of it ? And then the canoes may come back empty, so that a similar expedition has to be made in another direction !

What a terribly unromantic business life for one who came out to preach the religion of Jesus ! If he had not to conduct the morning and evening services in the schoolroom and to preach on Sundays, the Head could almost forget that he was a missionary at all ! But it is just by means of the Christian sympathy and gentleness that he shows in all this everyday business that he exercises his greatest influence ; whatever level of spirituality the community reaches is due to nothing so much as to the success of its Head in this matter of—Preaching without Words.

*

* *

A word now about the schools. A school to which children come for instruction while they live at home is impossible here because of the distances ; there are villages, for example, attached to the Lambarene Station, which are sixty or seventy miles away from it. The children must therefore live on the station, and the parents bring them in October and take them away in July when the big fishing expeditions begin. In return for the cost of their living the children, both boys and girls, do some sort of work, and their day is arranged very much as follows : From 7 to 9 in the morning they are at work cutting down grass and bush, for the defence of the station against invasion by the forest is in the main their task. When they have done all the clearing that is necessary at one end of the settlement they can always go to some other part where the undergrowth will have shot up again as it was before. From 9 to 10 is a rest hour, during which they breakfast ; from

10 to 12 there is school. The recreation time between 12 and 1 is usually spent in bathing and fishing. From 2 to 4 there is school again, and after that, work again for about an hour and a half. Some help in the cocoa plantation; the boys often go to the practical worker to help him, and they prepare bricks, carry building material where it is wanted, or finish digging or other work on the soil. Then the food for the following day is given out; at 6 comes the evening service, and after that they get supper ready. There is a big shed under which the children cook their bananas in native fashion, and they divide into groups of five or six, each of which has a pot and a fire hole to itself. At 9 they go to bed, that is, they retire to their plank bedsteads under the mosquito netting. On Sunday afternoons they make canoe expeditions, the mistress going out with a crew of girls. In the dry season they play on the sandbanks.

The work of the boys' school suffers, unfortunately, in this way, that when the evangelist goes out on his preaching rounds, or when a canoe expedition is needed for any purpose, a crew of boys has to be taken for it, and they may be absent for as much as a week. When shall we reach such a stage of efficiency that every mission station has its motor boat?

*

* *

Should a missionary have a thorough education? Yes. The better a man's mental life and his intellectual interests are developed, the better he will be able to hold out in Africa. Without this safeguard he is soon in danger of becoming a nigger, as it is called here. This shows itself in the way he loses every higher point of view; then his capacity for intellectual work diminishes, and he begins, just like a negro, to attach importance to, and to argue at any length about, the smallest matters. (In the matter of theology, too, the more thorough the training the better.)

That under certain circumstances a man may be a good missionary without having studied theology is proved by the example of Mr. Felix Faure, who at the present time is the Head of our station. He is by training an agricultural engineer (*ingénieur agronome*) and came to the Ogowe first of all to manage the station's agricultural land. At the same time he proved to be such an excellent preacher and evangelist that he became in time more missionary than planter.

I am not quite in agreement with the manner in which baptism is practised here. The rule is that only adults are baptised, it being felt that only those should be received into the Christian community whose way of life has stood some amount of testing.* But do we thereby build up a church on a broad and safe basis ? Is it essential that the communities shall be composed only of members of comparatively blameless life ? I think we must further consider the question of how they are to make sure of a normal stream of new members. If we baptise the children of Christian parents, we have growing up among us a number of natives who have been in the Church and under its influence from their childhood upwards. Certainly there will be some among them who show themselves unworthy of the Christian name given them in their childhood, but there

* Most Protestant missions practise infant baptism. There are some, however, who object to it. On the Ogowe, infant baptism is not customary, because the American missionaries, who founded the Protestant missions here, did not introduce it.—A. S.

will be many others who, just because they belong to the Church and find within it support in the dangers that surround them, become and remain loyal members of it.   Thus the question of infant baptism, which so disturbed the Church in the early centuries, comes up again to-day in the mission field as a live issue.   But if we wished to decide for infant baptism in the Ogowe district we should have in opposition to us nearly all the native evangelists and elders.

*

*   *

The most difficult problem in the mission field arises from the fact that evangelistic work has to be done under two banners, the Catholic and the Protestant. How much grander would be the work undertaken in the name of Jesus if this distinction did not exist, and there were never two churches working in competition. On the Ogowe, indeed, the missionaries of both bodies live in quite correct, sometimes in even friendly, relations with one another, but that does not remove the rivalry which confuses the native and hinders the spread of the Gospel.

I often visit the Catholic mission stations in my capacity of doctor and so have been able to gather a fairly clear idea of the way in which they conduct their evangelistic work and their education.   As to organisation, their missions seem to me to be better managed than ours in several ways.   If I had to distinguish between the aims which the two keep before them, I should say the Protestant mission puts in the first place the building up of Christian personalities, while the Catholic has in mind before all else the establishment on solid foundations of a church.   The former object is the higher one, but it does not take sufficient account of realities. To make the work of training permanently successful, a firmly established church, which grows in a natural way with the increase in the number of Christian families, is necessary. The church history of every period teaches this. Is it not the weakness as well as the greatness of Protestantism that it means personal religion too much and church too little ?

For the work which the American missionaries began here and the French have continued, I feel a hearty admiration. It has produced among the natives human and Christian characters which would convince the most decided opponents of missions as to what the teaching of Jesus can do for primitive man. But now we ought to have the men and the means to found more stations further inland, and so exert an educational influence on the natives before they are reached by the white man's trade and the dangers and problems which it brings with it for the child of nature.

Will this be possible within a measurable time ? What will be the lot of mission work after the war ? How will the ruined peoples of Europe be able to contribute any longer the necessary means for the various spiritual undertakings in the world ? There is, also, this further difficulty—that mission work can only flourish when it is to some extent international; but the war has made anything international impossible for a long time. And, lastly, missions throughout the world will soon feel that, owing to the war, the white race has lost a great deal of its spiritual authority over the coloured ones.

CHAPTER XI

CONCLUSION

FOR four years and a half we worked in Lambarene, but in the last of them we were able to spend the hot, rainy months between autumn and spring at the seaside. A white man who pitied my almost utterly exhausted wife put at our disposal, at the mouth of the Ogowe, two hours from Cape Lopez, a house which before the war had been the home of the man who watched his timber floats when they lay at anchor, but which had been empty since the trade came to a standstill. We shall never forget his kindness. Our principal food was herrings, which I caught in the sea. Of the abundance of fish in Cape Lopez Bay it is difficult for any one to form an adequate idea.

Around the house stood the huts in which the white man's labourers had lived when the trade was in full swing. Now, half ruined, they served as sleeping places for negroes who passed through. On the second day after our arrival I went to see whether there was any one in them, but no one answered my calls. Then I opened the doors one by one, and in the last hut saw a man lying on the ground with his head almost buried in the sand and ants running all over him. It was a victim of sleeping sickness whom his companions had left there, probably some days before, because they could not take him any further. He was past all help, though he still breathed. While I was busied with him I could see through the door of the hut the bright blue waters of the bay in their frame of green woods, a scene of almost magic beauty, looking still more enchanting in the flood of golden light poured over it by the setting sun. To be shown in a single glance such a paradise and such helpless, hopeless misery, was overwhelming . . . but it was a symbol of the condition of Africa.

On my return to Lambarene I found plenty to do, but this did not frighten me. I was fresh and vigorous again. Much of the work was caused just then by men who were ill with dysentery. Carriers for the military colony of the Cameroons had been impressed in our district, and many of them had caught the infection, but subcutaneous injections of emetin proved very effective even in the oldest cases.

When this levy of carriers was made, one of my patients who had a bad ulcer on his foot wanted to join as a volunteer, so that his brother, who had been taken, might not have to go alone. I represented to him that in three or four days he would fall out and be left on the roadside, where he would assuredly die. However, he would not let himself be convinced, and I almost had to use violence to keep him back.

I happened to be present when a body of impressed carriers who were to be taken to the Cameroons by water were embarked on the river steamer at N'Gômô. Then the natives began to know by experience what war really is. The vessel had started amid the wailing of the women ; its trail of smoke had disappeared in the distance, and the crowd had dispersed, but on a stone on the river bank an old woman whose son had

M

been taken sat weeping silently. I took hold of her hand and wanted to comfort her, but she went on crying as if she did not hear me. Suddenly I felt that I was crying with her, silently, towards the setting sun, as she was.

About that time I read a magazine article which maintained that there would always be wars, because a noble thirst for glory is an ineradicable element in the heart of man. These champions of militarism think of war only as idealised by ignorant enthusiasm or the necessity of self-defence. They would probably reconsider their opinions if they spent a day in one of the African theatres of war, walking along the paths in the virgin forest between lines of corpses of carriers who had sunk under their load and found a solitary death by the roadside, and if, with these innocent and unwilling victims before them, they were to meditate in the gloomy stillness of the forest on war as it really is.

✸

*   *

How shall I sum up the resulting experience of these four and a half years ? On the whole it has confirmed my view of the considerations which drew me from the world of learning and art to the primeval forest. " The natives who live in the bosom of Nature are never so ill as we are, and do not feel pain so much." That is what my friends used to say to me, to try to keep me at home, but I have come to see that such state- ments are not true. Out here there prevail most of the diseases which we know in Europe, and several of them—those hideous ones, I mean, which we brought here—produce, if possible, more misery than they do amongst us. And the child of nature feels them as we do, for to be human means to be subject to the power of that terrible lord whose name is Pain.

Physical misery is great everywhere out here. Are we justified in shutting our eyes and ignoring it because our European newspapers tell us nothing about it ? We civilised people have been spoilt. If any one of us is ill the doctor comes at once. Is an operation necessary, the door of some hospital or other opens to us immediately. But let every one reflect on the meaning of the fact that out here millions and millions live without help or hope of it. Every day thousands and thousands endure the most terrible sufferings, though medical science could avert them. Every day there prevails in many and many a far-off hut a despair which we could banish. Will each of my readers think what the last ten years of his family history would have been if they had been passed without medical or surgical help of any sort ? It is time that we should wake from slumber and face our responsibilities !

Believing it, as I do, to be my life's task to fight on behalf of the sick under far-off stars, I appeal to the sympathy which Jesus and religion generally call for, but at the same time I call to my help also our most fundamental ideas and reasonings. We ought to see the work that needs doing for the coloured folk in their misery, not as a mere " good work," but as a duty that must not be shirked.

Ever since the world's far-off lands were discovered, what has been the conduct of the white peoples to the coloured ones ? What is the meaning of the simple fact that this and that people has died out, that others are dying out, and that the condition of others is getting worse and worse as a result of their discovery by men who professed to be followers of Jesus ? Who can describe the injustice and the cruelties that in the course of centuries they have suffered at the hands of Europeans ? Who can measure the misery produced among them by the fiery drinks and the hideous diseases that we have taken to them ? If a record could be compiled of all that has happened between the white and the coloured races, it would make a book containing numbers of pages, referring to recent as well as to early times, which the reader would have to turn over unread, because their contents would be too horrible.

We and our civilisation are burdened, really, with a great debt. We are not free to confer benefits on these men, or not, as we please ; it is our duty. Anything we give them is not benevolence but atonement. For every one who scattered injury some one ought to go out to take help, and when we have done all that is in our power, we shall not have atoned for the thousandth part of our guilt. That is the foundation from which all deliberations about " works of mercy " out there must begin.

It goes without saying that Governments must help with the atonement, but they cannot do so till there already exists in society a conviction on the subject. The Government alone can never discharge the duties of humanitarianism ; from the nature of the case that rests with society and individuals.

The Government can send out as many colonial doctors as it has at its disposal, and as the colonial budgets are able to pay for. It is well known that there are great colonising powers which cannot find even enough doctors to fill the places of those already working in their colonies, though these are far from sufficient to cope with the need. So again, we see, the real burden of the humanitarian work must fall upon society and its individual members. We must have doctors who go among the coloured people of their own accord and are ready to put up with all that is meant by absence from home and civilisation. I can say from experience that they will find a rich reward for all that they renounce in the good that they can do.

Among the poor people out here they will not as a rule be able to collect the cost of their own living and work ; men must come forward at home who will provide what is necessary, and that is something that is due from all of us. But whom shall we get to make a beginning, without waiting till the duty is universally recognised and acted on ?

❦

*   *

The Fellowship of those who bear the Mark of Pain. Who are the members of this Fellowship ? Those who have learnt by experience what physical pain and bodily anguish mean, belong together all the world over ; they are united by a secret bond. One and all they know the horrors of suffering to which man can be exposed, and one and all they know the longing to be free from pain. He who has been delivered from pain must not think he is now free again, and at liberty to take life up just as it was before, entirely forgetful of the past. He is now a " man whose eyes are open " with regard to pain and anguish, and he must help to overcome those two enemies (so far as human power can control them) and to bring to others the deliverance which he has himself enjoyed. The man who, with a doctor's help, has been pulled through a severe illness, must aid in providing a helper such as he had himself, for those who otherwise could not have one. He who has been saved by an operation from death or torturing pain, must do his part to make it possible for the kindly anæsthetic and the helpful knife to begin their work, where death and torturing pain still rule unhindered. The mother who owes it to medical aid that her child still belongs to her, and not to the cold earth, must help, so that the poor mother who has never seen a doctor may be spared what she has been spared. Where a man's death agony might have been terrible, but could fortunately be made tolerable by a doctor's skill, those who stood around his death bed must help, that others, too, may enjoy that same consolation when they lose their dear ones.

Such is the Fellowship of those who bear the Mark of Pain, and on them lies the humanitarian task of providing medical help in the colonies. Their gratitude should be the source of the gifts needed. Commissioned by them, doctors should go forth to carry out among the miserable in far-off lands all that ought to be done in the name of civilisation, human and humane.

Sooner or later the idea which I here put forward will conquer the world, for with inexorable logic it carries with it the intellect as well as the heart.

But is just now the right time to send it out into the world ? Europe is ruined and full of wretchedness. With all the misery that we have to alleviate even under our very eyes, how can we think of far-off lands ?

Truth has no special time of its own. Its hour is now —always, and indeed then most truly when it seems most unsuitable to actual circumstances. Care for distress at home and care for distress elsewhere do but help each other if, working together, they wake men in sufficient numbers from their thoughtlessness, and call into life a new spirit of humanity.

But let no one say : " Suppose ' the Fellowship of those who bear the Mark of Pain ' does by way of beginning send one doctor here, another there, what is that to cope with the misery of the world ? " From my own experience and from that of all colonial doctors, I answer, that a single doctor out here with the most modest equipment means very much for very many. The good which he can accomplish surpasses a hundredfold what he gives of his own life and the cost of the material support which he must have. Just with quinine and arsenic for malaria, with novarsenobenzol for the various diseases which spread through ulcerating sores, with emetin for dysentery, and with sufficient skill and apparatus for the most necessary operations, he can in a single year free from the power of suffering and death hundreds of men who must otherwise have succumbed to their fate in despair. It is just exactly the advance of tropical medicine during the last fifteen years which gives us a power over the sufferings of the men of far-off lands that borders on the miraculous. Is not this really a call to us ?

For myself, now that my health, which since 1918 had been very uncertain, has been restored as the result of two operations, and that I have succeeded, by means of lectures and organ concerts, in discharging the debts which I had to incur during the war for the sake of my work, I venture to resolve to continue my activity among the suffering folk of whom I have written. The work, indeed, as I began it, has been ruined by the war. The friends from two nations who joined in supporting us, have been, alas ! deeply divided by what has happened in the world, and of those who might have helped us farther, many have been reduced to poverty by the war.   It will be very difficult to collect the necessary funds, which again must be far larger than before, for the expenses will be three times as heavy, however modestly I replan our undertaking.

Nevertheless, I have not lost courage. The misery I have seen gives me strength, and faith in my fellow-men supports my confidence in the future.   I do hope that I shall find a sufficient number of people who, because they themselves have been saved from physical suffering, will respond to requests on behalf of those who are in similar need. . . . I do hope that among the doctors of the world there will soon be several besides myself who will be sent out, here or there in the world, by " the Fellowship of those who bear the Mark of Pain."

St. Nicholas' Clergy House,
Strasbourg.
August, 1920.

INDEX

PRINTED IN GREAT BRITAIN BY THE WHITEFRIARS PRESS, LTD., TONBRIDGE.